THE ANATOMY OF NATURE

Books by Andreas Feininger

THE FACE OF NEW YORK

FEININGER ON PHOTOGRAPHY

NEW PATHS IN PHOTOGRAPHY

NEW YORK

ADVANCED PHOTOGRAPHY

SUCCESSFUL PHOTOGRAPHY

SUCCESSFUL COLOR PHOTOGRAPHY

THE CREATIVE PHOTOGRAPHER

CHANGING AMERICA

THE
ANATOMY
OF
NATURE

How function shapes the form
and design of animate
and inanimate structures
throughout the universe

by

ANDREAS FEININGER

CROWN PUBLISHERS, INC. · NEW YORK

American Book–Stratford Press, Inc., New York
Manufactured in the United States of America

FOREWORD

In a corner of my window which overlooks a wide Connecticut valley a spider has spun its web. Ever since it was so small that I could hardly see it, I have watched this spider grow and go about its way of life. And watching this exquisitely made and interesting little creature, I wondered why so many people have a horror of spiders and kill them on sight.

Few things in nature are more beautiful, functional, or unfathomable than an orb-spider's web. It is an incarnation of pure geometry, spun from silk whose tensile strength surpasses that of structural steel. In its center, motionless, the spider waits for insects to become enmeshed within its threads. This spider does not hunt for food. It is dependent upon chance captures for its survival. And it instinctively knows where to construct its web, to set its snare where insects will be bound to pass. It depends upon others. It cannot survive alone.

No living organism can survive without dependence upon other organisms. Each is an essential part of the great web of life, playing its small yet important role. Spiders are one of nature's regulating devices which prevent insects from reaching such numbers that they would destroy all plant life and themselves die of starvation. But without insects, many flowers and trees would not be pollinated and could not reproduce their kind. Without such plants, many animals could not exist. As a matter of fact, without green plants there would be neither animals nor man because both depend upon green plant life for their existence.

This is so because one of the necessities for life is carbon. Every molecule of every bit of living tissue must contain carbon. And although carbon is a constituent of the atmosphere, animals cannot absorb it from the air by breathing, but can obtain it only by eating plants.

This is the carbon cycle: carbon is united with oxygen to form carbon dioxide, one of the gases of the atmosphere. Through minute openings in their leaves, green plants absorb this gas. Within the leaf the gas is combined with water (absorbed by the roots and transported through the stem to the leaf) to form sugar. This process, known as photosynthesis, is powered by sunlight and engineered by chlorophyll, the green coloring matter of the leaf. Plant-eating animals obtain the carbon, without which they cannot build their tissues, by eating green plants. Flesh-eating animals obtain carbon by eating animals that have fed on plants.

Carbon is one of the earth's less abundant elements; carbon dioxide constitutes only 0.03% of the air's volume. Although animals exhale carbon, and green plants, too, return carbon dioxide to the atmosphere through respiration; and although some carbon is continually liberated through combustion of organic matter in fires and furnaces all over the world, and through volcanic seepage from the molten interior of the earth; nevertheless, all the carbon of the atmosphere would have been exhausted long ago—fixed within organic living matter or buried in the ground, as a large part is now buried in the form of coal, limestone, and oil—were it not for fungi and bacteria. Their role in the great cyclic drama of life is to break down dead organic matter into its basic components. And in doing this they free carbon to begin once more the cycle needed for all life. The carbon in your body cells may once have been part of a tree, an animal, or a primitive man living thousands of years ago. And in time this same carbon will help sustain another form of life.

Life cannot exist without nitrogen which, too, is an essential component of protoplasm. Nearly four-fifths of the atmosphere consists of nitrogen, but, as in the case of carbon, animals can absorb it only by eating plants, or indirectly by eating other animals. But green plants cannot absorb nitrogen as they can carbon from the air.

Again, it is left to certain kinds of bacteria to complete the cyclic web of life. Living symbiotically in the roots of many plants, particularly legumes, from which they obtain their carbon, these nitrogen-fixing bacteria have a unique power. They are able to absorb the life-giving nitrogen directly from the air and convert it into proteins. These proteins are absorbed by the roots of the plants from whose protoplasms the bacteria obtained their food. Dead and decaying, decomposed by saprophytes—fungi living on dead organic matter—and broken down into basic compounds by ammonifying bacteria, these plants in time surrender their borrowed nitrogen to the soil to be drawn upon by new plants according to their need. Or the plants provide the animals or men who eat them with their essential nitrogen which after death is returned to the soil to be recycled again.

Not only are animals and plants dependent upon one another, eternally linked by need, but plants are also linked to plants and animals to animals—as man is linked to man—and one cannot survive without the other. Consider stem rust of wheat, a parasitic fungus which in certain years has caused the loss of some hundred million bushels of wheat in the United States. To complete its life cycle, this fungus is dependent upon two entirely unrelated plants, wheat and barberry. During the summer, the parasite first appears on the wheat as reddish postules in which spores are formed. Wind carries these spores to other wheat plants where each develops and produces another postule from which more spores will appear, spreading the disease from field to field. Shortly before the wheat plant matures, the fungus produces a second type spore which is black and, fastened to the wheat stubble and straw, survives the winter. In spring these black spores germinate, each growing into a fungus plant consisting of four cells, each of which in turn produces a single spore of a third type. These, the basidiospores, travel with the wind but can no longer live on wheat. Only if they fall on a barberry plant can they germinate and in time produce two new types of spore, the plus and minus spermatium. These develop on the barberry leaf and, after fertilization, produce a fifth type of spore, the aeciospore. In order to survive and complete the life cycle of the fungus, the aeciospore must be carried by the wind to a young wheat plant. Here the fungus grows within the tissues of the plant and once again produces the red spores with which its life cycle began.

A rather complicated life cycle which shows the interdependence of animal upon animal is that of the broad fish tapeworm which is rather common in the Great Lakes region and can grow to a length of sixty feet. To develop and mature, the eggs of this tapeworm must reach water where the larvae hatch. In turn, these larvae must be eaten by crabs and the crabs by fish. Man, the ultimate host in which the worm matures and lays its eggs, becomes infected by the parasite if he eats insufficiently cooked infected fish.

My tiny spider has caught a tinier fly and is busy trussing it up with threads of silk. It occurs to me as I watch this deft operation that, although I can clearly see the spider, the spider cannot see me. We live on levels so completely different that the denizens of the lower one do not even know that the higher one exists. And the disquieting idea occurs to me that, perhaps, there are levels still higher than mine, and that I, too, am watched by something so immensely big that it is forever outside my ken.

As a matter of fact, what proof do I have that mine

is the highest level? Not very long ago man believed that the earth was the center of the universe. Then he found out that it actually is nothing but a speck of dust in a galaxy so vast that it staggers the imagination. And today he knows that even this immense galaxy is only one of millions of similar galaxies that drift in space of such titanic dimensions that he had to invent the light-year to measure it. A light-year is the distance which light, traveling at a speed of some 186,000 miles per second, covers in one year—some six trillion miles. And today, man's horizon in space—the distance to which he has penetrated the universe with the eyes of giant telescopes—lies two billion times six trillion miles away. Even then there is no indication of an end of the universe.

Against the background of his universe, man appears smaller than the smallest virus in relation to man. I can no more fathom the true nature of my universe than a virus swimming in the stream of my blood or living in a cell of my body can gauge the nature of its world.

Scientists have discovered that matter consists of atoms, and that atoms consist of a nucleus surrounded by electrons. They have also discovered that the structure of the atom is such that it consists mostly of empty space, since the distances between the particles of the atom are relatively immense. If we could enlarge the nucleus of an atom to the size of a cherry, its electrons could be represented by mosquitoes buzzing around in circles of more than a mile in diameter. Similarly, matter, too, is mostly empty space. The distances between neighboring atoms are relatively so vast that the "cherries" would be spaced hundreds of miles apart. If it were possible to squeeze all the empty space out of a man, his body would be reduced to a barely visible speck. And if one of the electrons whirling planet-like around the sun-like nucleus of a calcium atom in one of the cells of my bones were inhabited by subatomic beings, such beings contemplating their subatomic universe would, just like me, feel dwarfed by the immensity of their "cosmic space." And the awesome thought comes to my mind that, since the structures of the atom and the universe appear to be so similar, perhaps still bigger systems might exist in which the solar system is only an atom, and the universe is the substance of a super-being which man calls Nature or God.

At first, such a thought may seem fantastic. Yet actually it is no more fantastic than the scientifically accepted facts that physical space has no boundaries, stops nowhere and yet is infinite; that the velocity of light appears the same to all observers, regardless of whether they travel toward or away from its source at no matter how high a speed; that the electron possesses the properties both of a solid hard particle and a group of waves; that electron waves are not "real" waves but "waves of probability"; or that, in the final analysis, our own bodies consist of "waves of probability" and empty space.

Toward the end of the last century, scientists were convinced that the physical universe was almost thoroughly explored; that they knew most of the answers to the problems of the universe; and that the few remaining mysteries were on the threshold of solution. Everything, they thought, could be explained in terms of the Newtonian concepts of matter, gravitation, space, and time, and the great British physicist Lord Kelvin declared that he could understand nothing of which he could not make a working model.

Today this mechanistic explanation of the universe, regarded as hopelessly inadequate, has been abandoned. Recent discoveries in atomic and subatomic physics and refinements in our methods of observation have disclosed a wealth of new facts which cannot possibly be explained in Newtonian terms. At a contemporary physicists' convention, Lord Kelvin would feel as inadequate as a high-school student.

Actually, the more we learn about the true nature of matter and space, the more do we realize how little we really know because almost each new discovery raises more questions than it answers, opening vistas into new unimaginable realms. Today the universe appears more mysterious than ever before, and our understanding of nature has reached a point where it is no longer possible to interpret scientific findings in common-sense terms. Trying to translate into mechanistic images related to everyday experience many of the mathematical formulas used by modern scientists to describe complex physical phenomena is as futile as trying to recognize realistic objects in a modern abstract painting. And slowly the realization begins to dawn that, just as even the most intelligent animals will never be able to understand (except, perhaps, on the most superficial level) the functioning of man's creations, so also man himself, despite his marvelous brain, may be congenitally unable ever fully to comprehend the functioning of the work of a superior Creator—the universe.

Nevertheless, men of science feel that nature has a plan, a purpose, and its own design. For a while it seemed that Newton's laws expressed nature's plan. Later, the laws of relativity were recognized as only *part* of nature's organization. Evolution is seen as another part. Investigation continues in the separate fields and perhaps, one day, a great intellect similar to Einstein's will correlate all of the phases of the design—all of the scientific findings—into one comprehensive plan.

So far, science has not provided all the answers. It describes but does not always explain. Although scientists can measure with superb accuracy the frequencies of the electromagnetic radiation which we perceive as color, they are unable to explain how the sensation of color occurs within the brain. Nor can they explain the psychological effects of color, or the enjoyment which we can derive from color harmonies. Or from music. Or from works of art. But we do not need to understand to be able to enjoy. We understand intellectually, but we enjoy emotionally—we feel. Few people understand the physics of color, but most feel moved by the beauty of a flaming sunset sky. It is in this sense, through feeling and sympathy, that I attempt on the following pages to show the reader some of the wonders which surround us—some of the manifestations of nature's design.

As I look at the web of my little spider it seems to me—the former architect and engineer—a structure worthy of as much admiration as any structure created by man. Like any creation of nature, it is functional, designed for a definite purpose, constructed with marvelous economy to achieve maximum efficiency with a minimum expenditure of material and weight. It has clarity and symmetry of organization. And it derives from these basic qualities a particular kind of beauty which far surpasses that of man's ornamental design. A spider web has the elemental beauty that is inherent in any truly functional form. It is the same sort of beauty that we find in the symbols of Euclidean geometry, in ballistic curves, and

in the crystals of snow. We also find it in flower shapes which nature did not design as objects of beauty but as devices of propagation. We recognize it in shapes of bones which, rivaling modern sculpture in abstract beauty, are formed to bear the strains and stresses to which they are subjected. We see such beauty in nature wherever we look and, although we often may not comprehend what underlies it, the more closely we look the more we find to enjoy. No one has given better expression to this than Dr. Roman Vishniac, superb photographer of nature's manifestations, who once said: "Everything made by human hands looks terrible under magnification—crude, rough, and unsymmetrical. But in nature every bit of life is lovely. And the more magnification we use, the more details are brought out, perfectly formed, like endless sets of boxes within boxes."

As long as I can remember I have been interested in the forms of rocks and plants and animals. I have studied them, not with the eye of the artist, but with the eye of the architect and engineer who is primarily attracted by structure, construction, and function. A great number of picture books have been compiled to show people that nature is beautiful. But the type of beauty stressed in those books is, in my opinion, the superficial kind of beauty of form evaluated solely as ornament without consideration of function and purpose. Nature is never beautiful in this sense. If things in nature are beautiful, their beauty is not superficial but the resultant form of definite purpose. In the main, nature is practical—much more so than man. Its forms are functional forms derived from necessity. And precisely because in the best sense of the word they are functional, these forms are beautiful.

In the work of man, we find and appreciate this kind of functional beauty in the sleek shapes of jet planes, in the parabolic curves of a suspension bridge, in the forms of modern microscopes. Because modern man has finally discovered the elemental beauty of functional form—form freed from superficial ornamentation—he has begun to appreciate it for its own sake. It is from this point of view that I have approached the functional forms in nature.

As I examined them, I found that certain entirely unrelated objects of nature were constructed according to the same basic principles. Layers of water-deposited sediments and the annual growth rings of wood, for example, if rendered in the same scale (pp. 28-29), looked almost identical, indicating that the records of time and accretion are manifested in quite the same way in both wood and rock. The stiffening veins of a leaf and those of an insect's wing represent the identical principle although one is manifest in a plant and the other in an animal (pp. 62-63). And protective spines are essentially the same whether found in a plant, a mammal, an insect, or a mollusk (pp. 16 and 102-103). Everything is created from the same basic elements. And atoms combine to form molecules, and molecules to form matter, in only a limited number of ways. But at what point do they come to life? Where does one draw the line between things living and inanimate? Dead crystals grow as if they were alive, and live viruses, when desiccated, crystallize like minerals, only to come back to life again when conditions are right. Actually, in the last analysis, all the elements of which living organisms consist are nothing but inanimate matter—atoms, elements, chemical compounds—and yet together they constitute life.

It is the purpose of this book to document the unity of natural things, their interdependence, and their similarity; to show the beauty of the living functional form; perhaps to foreshadow the ultimate findings of science—a simple universal plan; and to make you feel related to the rocks and the plants and the animals—you, an integral part of nature, a part of the universe.

ANDREAS FEININGER

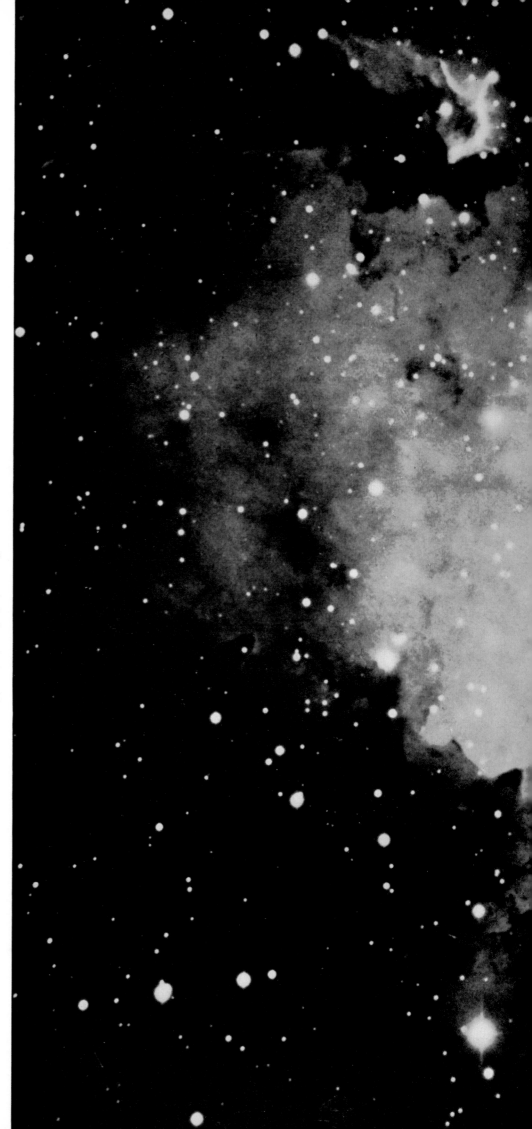

Gen. 1:3: And God said, Let there be light: and there was light.

This photograph can truly be called a picture of creation: it shows chaos and darkness yielding to order, form, and light.

This is a nebula—NGC 6611 in Scutum—a cloud of swirling cosmic gas billions of miles wide excited to incandescence by the radiation of neighboring stars and expanding into space with the force of an explosion.

The gas is hydrogen, and the hydrogen atom—the simplest of all atoms, consisting of only one proton and one electron —is the building stone of the universe. In the nuclear furnaces of the stars, hydrogen is transformed into the hundred-odd elements that make up the universe including our planet—its water and air, rocks, plants, and animals, man himself, and everything created by man. It is within nebulae such as this that through condensation stars are born.

Courtesy Mt. Wilson and Palomar Observatories

Stars are not evenly distributed throughout space. Instead, they congregate to form immense "island-universes"—the galaxies—each gradually and organically evolved from a primeval cloud of cosmic gas, separated from one another by distances so unimaginably vast that it takes light, travel-ing at a speed of some 186,000 miles per *second,* a million *years* and more to bridge the intervening space.

The fantastic object shown above floating serenely in space is a galaxy—NGC 4594, the "Sombrero Hat"—one of the hundred million-odd galaxies that have been

recorded with the aid of giant telescopes. It probably contains more than a hundred billion stars—each an enormous radiant "sun"—and is surrounded by hundreds of globular clusters each consisting of another hundred thousand-odd stars. The dark band surrounding this galaxy is formed by clouds of cosmic dust. Its distance is estimated at close to ten million parsecs—and a parsec equals 19,200 billion miles.

Courtesy Mt. Wilson and Palomar Observatories

The fiery pinwheel at left—NGC 5194-5, the "Whirlpool" in Canes Venatici—typifies a spiral galaxy, a common form of stellar aggregation. Our own galaxy, the Milky Way, is believed to have a similar structure. We cannot see its spiral arms because we are within the galaxy itself, surrounded on all sides by stars.

The unimaginable number of stars comprising a typical spiral galaxy—estimated at between two hundred and four hundred billion "suns"—is made somewhat tangible when one looks at the photograph above which shows only a minute section of the Milky Way. Each speck of white represents a star, a monstrous mass of incandescent gas as large or larger than the sun. Yet against the background of the cosmic void, the sun is only an infinitesimal speck of dust, insignificant, immaterial. Only to us is the sun the heart of the universe.

Courtesy Mt. Wilson and Palomar Observatories

Morning in the forest. With the force of an explosion, created some eight minutes earlier, ninety-three million miles away in the thermonuclear furnace of the sun, the light of a new day bursts upon the forest. A new morning, a new day—a measure of change and evolution—birth, growth, maturity, decline, death, and decay—and out of decaying matter new life rising again.

Walk on a dew-fresh morning in the forest and attune yourself to your environment until you feel part of it. You will find wonders in the immense diversity of life, the intricacy of its manifestations. Wherever you look, there is life. A dormant seed, small as a grain of sand, bears within its tiny shell the future flowering plant. A squirrel watches from its perch, half-hidden behind the trunk of a tree. A deermouse scurries in the underbrush. A spider waits patiently in its web. Armies of caterpillars chew away the leaves. Each life depends upon another, pursuing or pursued in the great battle for survival, the vanquished furnishing the victor with a meal. Worms tunnel the ground converting leaf mold to humus. Fungi and bacteria break down decaying matter into organic compounds which in time will nourish new life.

The air itself vibrates with sound and motion, the wingbeats of insects, the song and call of birds, the ceaseless whispering of boughs and leaves rustled by the gentle morning winds.

You become aware of the interdependence of all life, animals and plants, all of nature's creatures, each dependent upon others for sustenance or protection. And you realize with sharp clarity that you, too, are part of this immensity of nature, a humble yet important part, earth-bound, mortal, dependent for survival upon animal and plant, and that the molecules and atoms that constitute your body are identical with those that compose the rocks, the plants, the animals, the earth, moon, sun, and stars

Small pine cones lying dormant on the forest floor bear within their woody shells the seeds that in time will grow to towering trees like those whose trunks are shown on the facing page. What a marvel that each tiny seed, small as the head of a match, contains the pattern for a giant tree, complete with all its diversifications into wood and bark and flowers and leaves, trunk, branches, root, and crown; latent, invisible, yet ready to burst forth with elementary force when conditions are right—in growth rooting to the dark earth, reaching sunward to reproduce its kind.

Compare the seeds from various plants: many look more or less alike, some are even indistinguishable from one another. And yet, inevitably, each of these seeds will develop into one predestined type of plant and no other, containing not only the structural pattern of this plant with its diversification into root, stem, flower, and leaf, but also the characteristics of the species—the typical form of the leaf, the shape and color of the flower, down to the last most minute detail. Nowhere in nature, perhaps, can the mystery of creation be felt more strongly than in the contemplation of a seed.

Sugar maple
in Connecticut

The same tree
in winter

Each living thing grows in accordance with the pattern typical for its species. This pattern is most clearly expressed in its supporting structure—the skeleton of vertebrates, the shell of snails, the woody trunk and branches of trees. To the initiated, a bare tree in winter is just as recognizable as belonging to a certain species as in summer when it bears its characteristic leaves.

White
ash trees
in spring

To take up water from the soil, to brace themselves against the sweep of winds plants anchor to the earth with roots. Activated by gravitational forces, roots unerringly thrust toward the soil. The might of the driving root, sinking anchor in the earth, is almost beyond comprehension—splitting rocks, cracking concrete and masonry, lifting boulders inches from their bed. Such strength is evident in the crushing grip of the knotted roots which hold this fig tree to the ground.

Lacking structural rigidity, vines and lianas, destined to cling to stronger form, anchor with both root and tendril.

With feelers as sensitive as fingers a grape vine probes the air for a hold.

The coiled springlike tendrils of a passion flower magnified ten times linear.

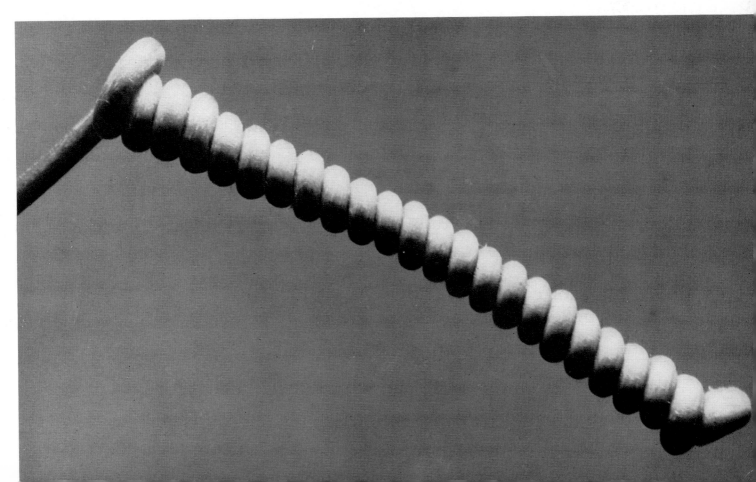

Ground fettered, incapable of escape through flight, plants are endowed with special means of protection. Some, like the cacti above, are covered with bristling spines as a de- fense against leaf-eating animals. Others, like the poison ivy plant at right, produce an invisible oil which upon contact blisters the skin and tongue of those who venture too close or dare to take a bite.

To insure the spread of their species, plants have developed a multitude of ingeniously engineered devices for dispersing their seeds. Some hook to the coats of animals and fall away as they rove. Others are dispersed by birds who feed upon their fruit but eliminate the indigestible seeds. Still others fall to closer ground, shot to distances of several yards when the drying fruits split open with a snap.

Some travel with ocean currents and tides, remaining buoyant for months, retaining power to germinate and grow on distant island soils. But the greatest number travel with the winds, gliding on gossamer parachute like the dandelion seeds; spinning in spiral flight and fall, on miniature propeller forms, like the maple seeds; or whirling in rolling race with prairie winds to shake from the parent husk, like the seeds of the tumbleweed.

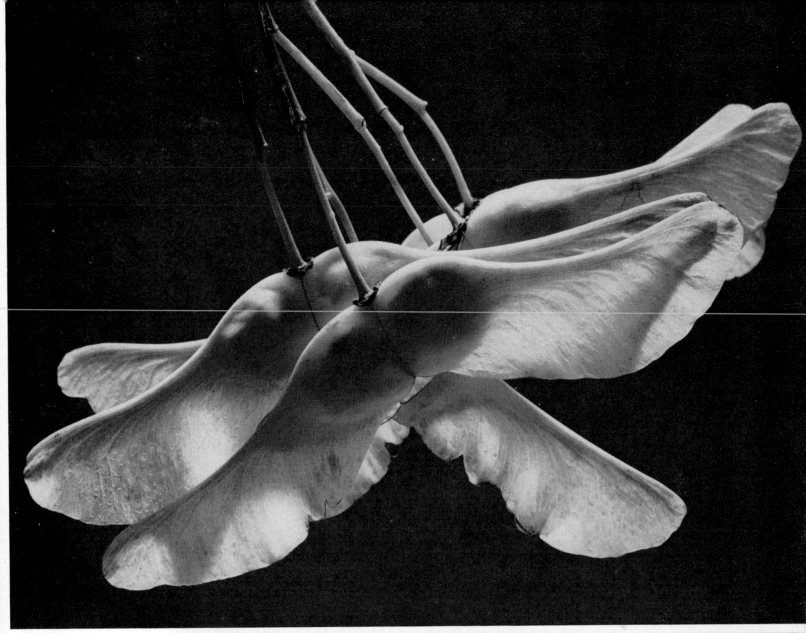

Maple seeds

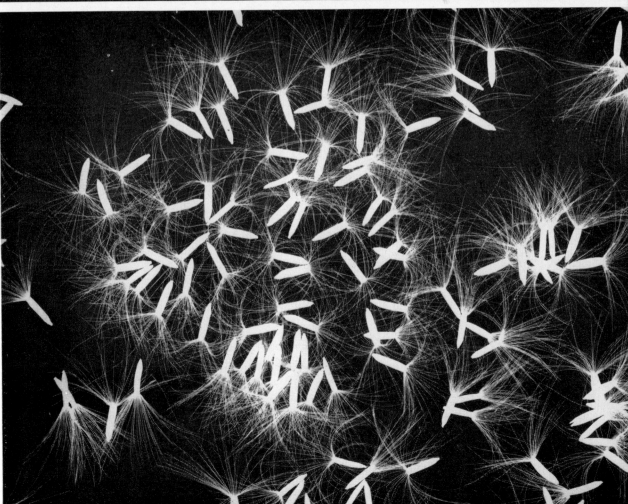

Rattlesnake weed seeds

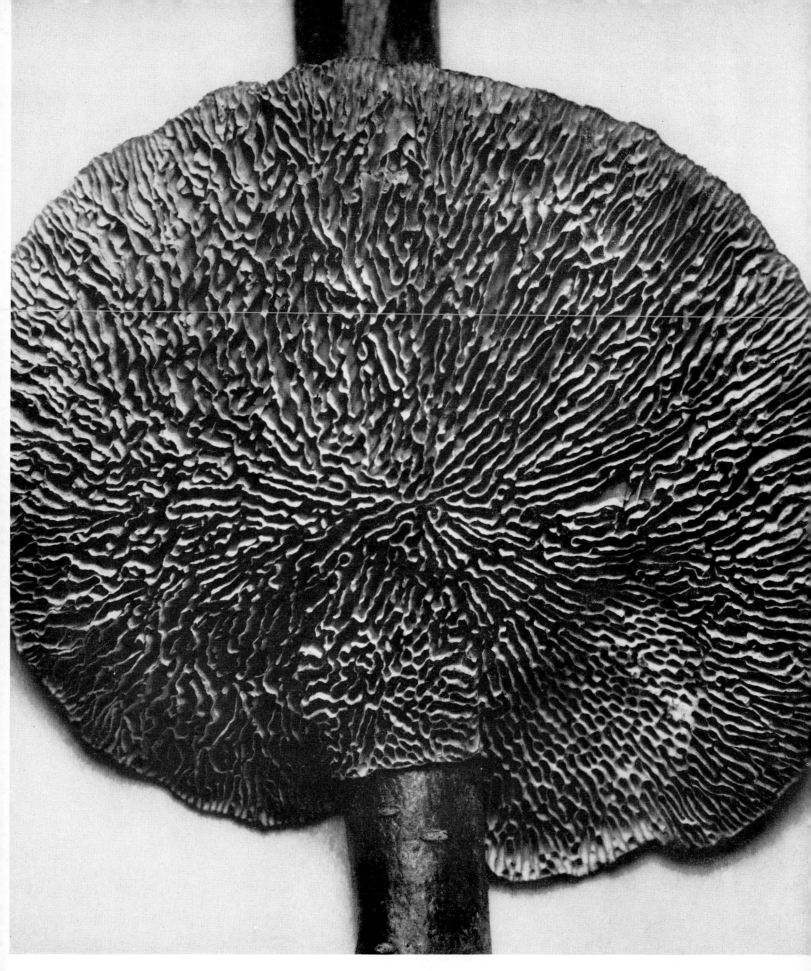

Magnified seven times, these are the gills of a fungus on which the spores grow.

Though nature is magnificent in its abundance, much of what it produces is expendable. Some fungi—the puffballs —contain up to seven-thousand billion spores within a single parent plant. Yet of this unimaginable number possibly only one in a trillion matures.

Tumbleweed, its wind-propelled journey ended in a juniper tangle in an arroyo in New Mexico.

In the swampy New England woodlands, the skunk cabbage green heralds spring, pressing in tightly furled form upward through frozen soil (*left*) to unfold its bright broad leaves to the first warm rays of the sun (*above*). To penetrate through such ground and withstand the cold of early spring, these plants generate heat through rapid growth and expansion. The internal temperature of skunk cabbage plants pushing up through frozen soil has been found to be as much as twenty-seven degrees Fahrenheit higher than that of their surroundings and ten to twenty degrees above the freezing point.

When their allotted time is up, all living things must die and surrender their place to the new generations which they helped to create. Otherwise the world would soon be so overcrowded with living organisms, fighting and killing one another in a desperate struggle for food, that none could live its given time at peace. And yet, in a universal sense, life is immortal. For the living reproductive cell plasm is passed on from one generation to the next, and the basic compounds of living things revert to the soil to sustain new life—the soil giving life to plants that in turn provide sustenance for animals which in turn sustain other animals or man—life cycle flowing into life cycle in a never-ending round.

Shown here is a dying pinyon pine near the rim of the Grand Canyon. And another that has already fallen in death, returning its borrowed substance to the soil.

Because the laws of nature are universal, completely un-related things often bear a striking similarity. This becomes evident in the structures of wood and sedimentary rock, both formed layer by layer in a process of accretion—each layer added by a season's growth, a year, a period of dry-ness, flood, or inundation. Thus nature accurately records the passage of time in terms of growing seasons, flood or drought, or periods when the land stood above water or was submerged beneath it. These layers in wood (*left*) and rock (*above*) contain nature's records of the earth.

A small piece of charred wood, magnified approximately ten times its natural size, shows the growth rings of a tree.

A section of a clam shell, magnified twenty times linear, shows the structure of the shell which the growing mollusk builds up layer by layer.

Sediments deposited layer by layer in shallow water in ancient times uplifted to form this mountain.

Shale—formed of sedimentation and pressure from overlaying rocks—eroded by the action of frost and running water, reveals its layered structure.

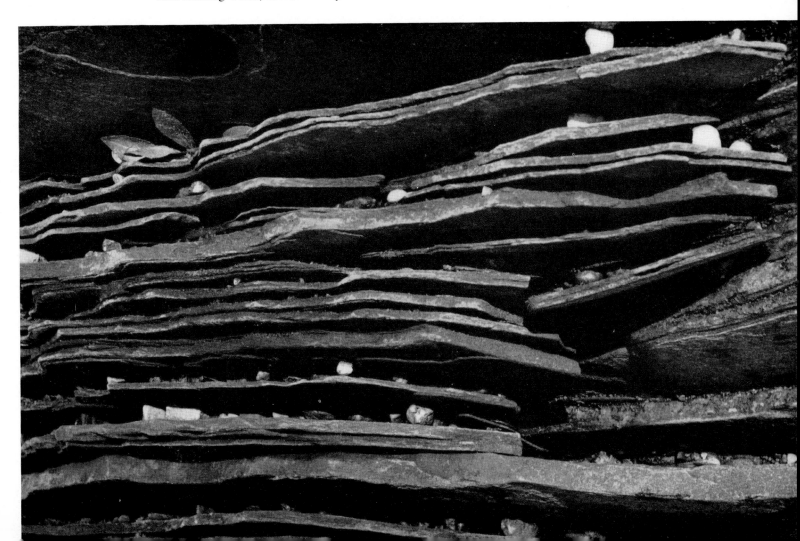

This is the inside of a mountain—cut in half by water's powerful eroding force—its size indicated by the pines that grow precariously along its narrow ledges. The layers of sediment, marking specific periods in time, are clearly visible. The cross-bedding—the minor beds oblique to the main strata—indicates the direction of the wind or flowing water which deposited the grains of sand that formed these layers.

Millions of years ago, swept by wind and water from the fine debris of still more ancient mountains leveled by erosion, numberless grains of quartz were deposited to form this cross-bedded sandstone. Now these very rocks are worn away by erosion's force, their change documenting the ceaseless cycle of construction and destruction that eternally runs through nature.

Sliced by a stream, this sand dune formed recently by the Colorado River (*below*) shows cross-bedding on a miniature scale (note the scale indicating size of the weed at right), revealing the fact that despite its smooth surface even a sand dune is not homogeneous but has, as a result of growth through accretion, a complex internal structure.

The stream-cut bank at right is formed of alternating layers of gravel and sand. First deposited by water, now breaking down to water's flow, it documents the constant change of the land.

The imprint of water's rippling flow retained in plastic river mud.

Hardened into stone, fossil ripple marks, identical with the marks in the mud, prove that these rocks were formed from sediment deposited in shallow water.

When the waters of flash floods recede, the mud and silt which they deposited dries and through loss of volume shrinks and cracks. This picture shows the building-up of the land by deposit of water-carried sands and clays.

Flood-deposited mud dries to curling broken-saucer shapes, their edges revealing their layered structure.

In drying broken to fine flakes, a thin coat of mud, rain-spotted, peels like weathered paint.

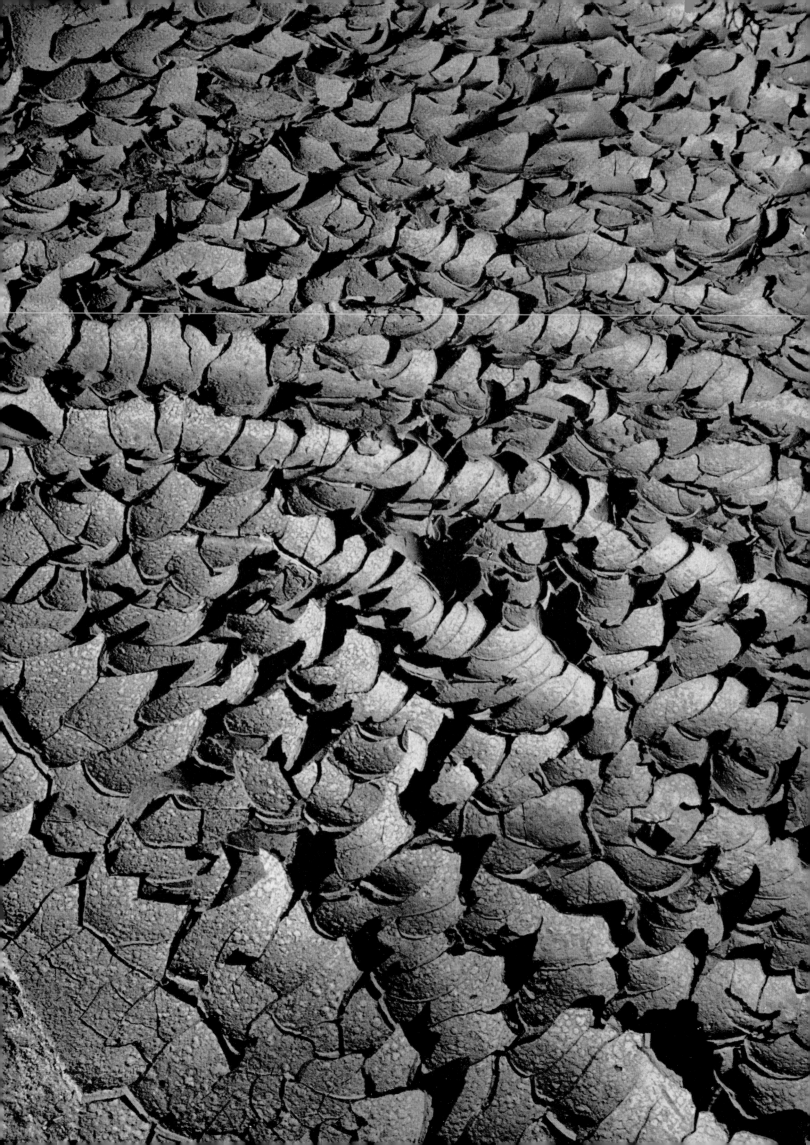

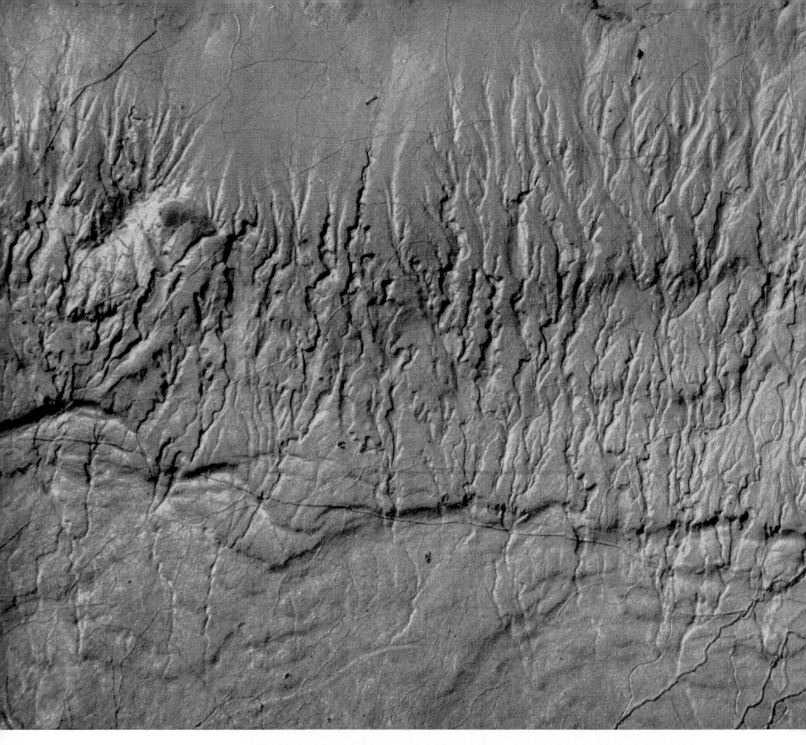

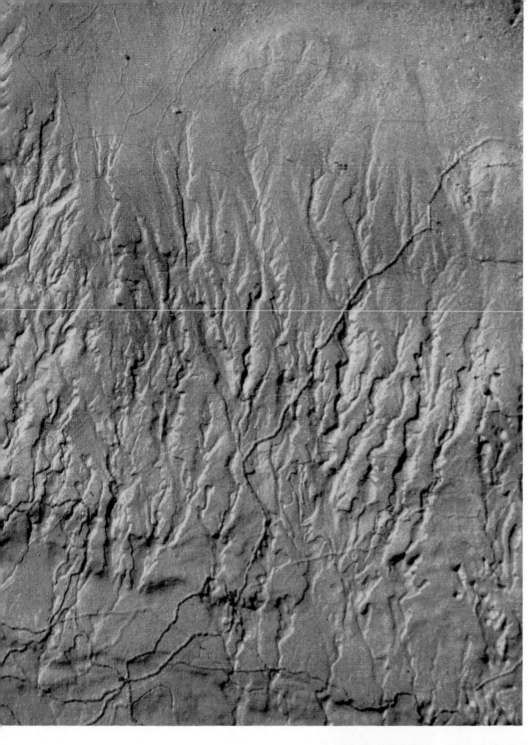

Erosion manifested on the smallest scale. Drops of rain sweep away sand grains and mud, etching the soil with fine erosive lines. And though the patterns on these pages in reality cover areas only inches wide, aerial photographs of mountainous sections of the land often show erosion formations that are very similar. The forces which created these small patterns, multiplied millions of times, incessantly cut the massive face of the earth into different forms.

(*Left*) Though still relatively small in scale (note fence post in upper right-hand corner), erosion of this highway embankment repeats the pattern which, on a tremendous scale, is seen in the spectacular formations in Utah's Bryce Canyon.

(*Above*) Sandstone corrugated to "rills" by run-off water which dissolved the cement that once bound the sand grains together.

(*Right*) Close-up of a disintegrating sandstone boulder, pock-marked by rain that leached out the binding cement. In nature, change is the only permanence, and even rocks must decay.

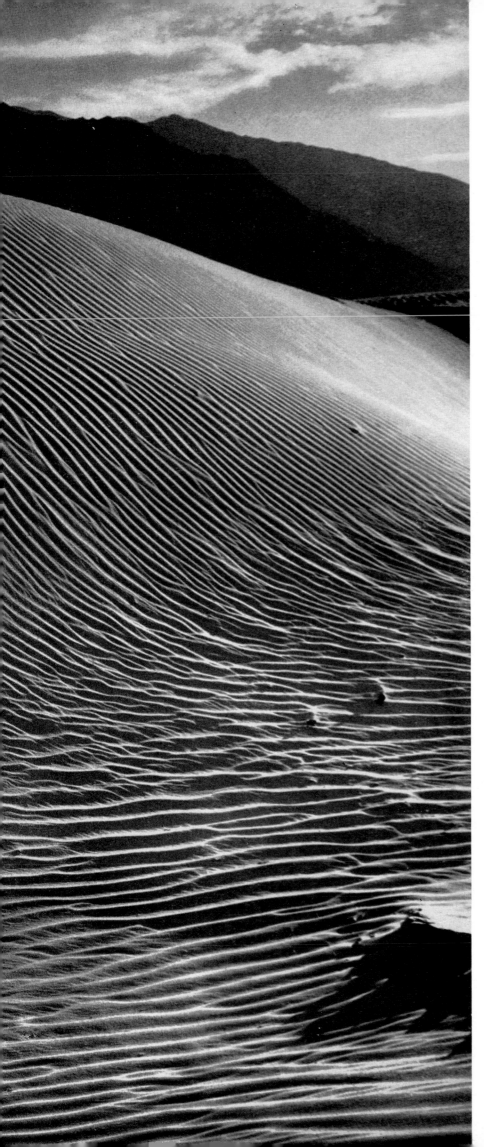

The clean wind-rippled sands of these tremendous dunes in California's Death Valley were once solid granite high up in the near-by Cottonwood Mountains. Sheared away by heat and frost, leveled from their heights by rain and mountain streams, boulders, rocks, and mineral debris descend, collecting at the mountain's base and spilling out upon the floor of the valley in the form of great alluvial fans. Here, in the blistering desert sun, this debris quickly dries and ceaseless winds pick up the pulverized material and pile it up into immense, constantly shifting dunes of sand.

45

Though its vast space appears forbidding and inhospitable in its aridity, the desert is not devoid of life. No part of this earth is entirely sterile, for life adapts to the most adverse conditions. Organisms live in the sulphur-exuding vents of geysers in steaming waters just below the boiling point; in the icy arctic; in the ever-dark depths of the sea; in the desiccating dryness of the desert. Nocturnal to escape the shriveling heat of the sun, sleeping throughout the day in holes, in crevices, under rocks, in the scant shade of thorny shrubs, desert animals—lizards, antelope, ground squirrels, kangaroo mice, kit foxes, coyotes—go forth in the cool of night in search for food, the sands charting their wanderings.

Water—briefly held in a spider's web . . .

Water—vaporizing to clouds and atmospheric mist . . . .rising as steam from bubbling geysers . . .

Water—in the process of freezing, changing from the liquid to the solid state as water molecule aligns itself to water molecule in regular crystalline pattern to harden into sparkling plumes of ice.

Ice feathers on a window pane and feathers of a bird—completely unrelated objects yet so similar in appearance that one wonders where the division may be between the living and the inanimate; whether in reality such a division exists; or if everything nature-created is to some degree alive. . . .

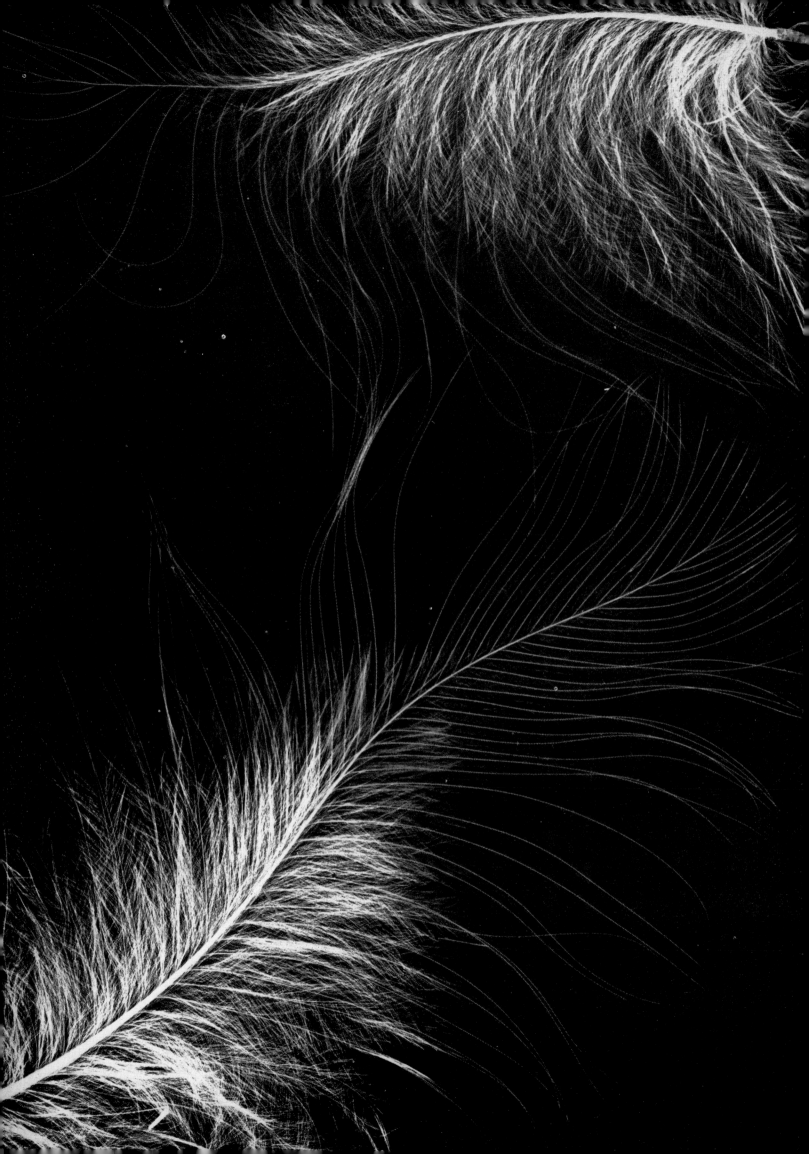

Electric discharge pattern, photographed by Professor A. von Hippel, Massachusetts Institute of Technology, Cambridge, Massachusetts.

Fairchild Aerial Surveys, Inc.

Aerial view of some tributaries of the Colorado River.

Governed by the universal "law of least resistance," currents of electricity and water form similar flow patterns as they draw together and unite at the "lowest point."

The photograph at left brings to mind feathers (like those on the previous page) and certain unicellular animals, whereas the picture above suggests a leafless tree—similarities caused perhaps more by design than by accident. Living things, as well as the subjects of these pictures, are made up of molecules, atoms, and electrons. When these particles combine in "growth," they follow the same basic laws regardless of whether the combination occurs in animate or inanimate matter. Such similarities provide the stuff of which theories about the universe are made.

A cissus leaf and a grasshopper wing. Though one is part of a plant and the other of an animal, the engineering problems underlying both are the same: a membrane must be stiffened to become self-supporting. In both cases the

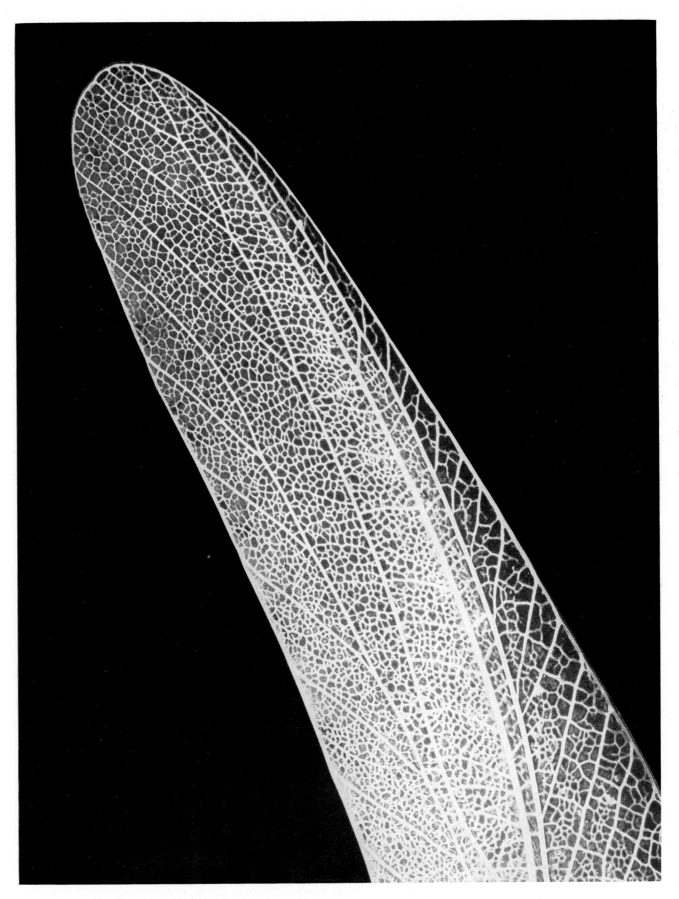

solution is based upon a main rib from which a system of more or less parallel secondary veins branch off, which in turn are connected by an irregular network of small auxiliary veins, resulting in strikingly similar structures.

Head and antennae of a male Luna moth, magnified approximately twenty times linear.

Head and thorax of a clothes moth, magnified approximately one hundred times linear.

Out of the night, lured by the glow of man-made light, strange creatures emerge and swirl in bumpy flight before screens and windows. Popularly but erroneously lumped together as "bugs" (the bugs comprise only one specific order of insects; their best known representative is the

bedbug), these insects are as varied in appearance as mammals or birds. Because of their great variety of fantastic shapes and colors, they provide the appreciative observer with an unending source of enjoyment and surprise.

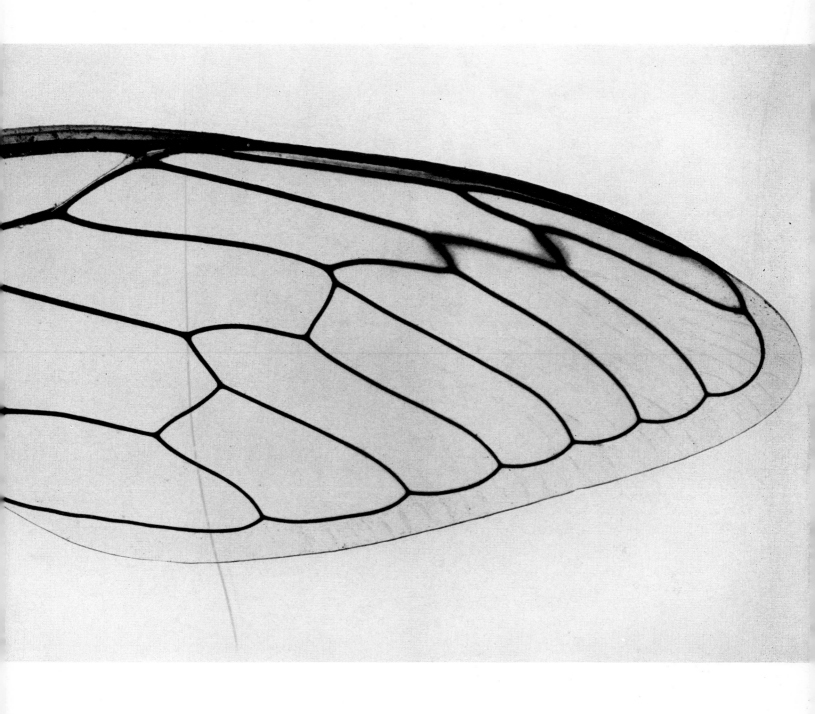

Everything in nature is designed for a purpose, whether
it is the shape and color of a flower, the placement of
leaves along a branch, or the scales on the butterfly's wing
which are shown in a close-up on the facing page. The
more closely we look at objects of nature the more beauty
we find within that purposefulness of design as exempli-
fied by these two insect wings—the beauty that is clarity
of organization, economy of material, symmetry of shape,
perfection of execution—qualities inherent in every form
of nature.

The arrangements of these leaves form aesthetically pleasing designs. In their creation, however, nature was not concerned

with beauty but with effective function—patterns organized
in such a way that each leaf receives its full share of light.

The strange and beautiful shapes of the agave (*above*) and the Joshua trees (*facing page*) are products of necessity, evolved through the ages to a state of the most effective protection against animal enemies, desiccation, and heat. Native to arid and semitropical lands, the first requirement for survival of these plants is conservation of water— their leaves are thick, narrow, and hard, offering only a tough and relatively small surface to evaporation. And since they are almost the only evergreen plants of their region, the second requirement for survival is protection against plant-eating animals, which is provided by the needle-pointed daggerlike shapes of their leaves.

A plant designed to thrive in the sun: prickly pear cactus—small, thick, fleshy leaves turn their narrow edges to the sun, presenting a minimum surface to dehydration.

A plant designed to thrive in the shade: Virginia creeper—thin, large, widely spread leaves arranged in a natural mosaic, to prevent one leaf from shading another, turn maximum surfaces to the light.   73

Nature's inventiveness is limitless, and the number of different forms that its creations take is as large as the number of species: some 840,000 known kinds of animals, close to 350,000 different plants. But such variety is not for variety's sake. Each form differs from all others solely because it is adapted most perfectly to a set of given conditions and plays one specific part in the whole of life.

Not only are the overall shapes of living things of an unending variety, but also the different parts of which each consists. The more closely we observe nature the more we find to marvel at, such as the tentacles of the passion flower (*above*) charged with latent power like a coiled spring; or the reed stalk on the facing page which rivals a Greek column in beauty and grace of design.

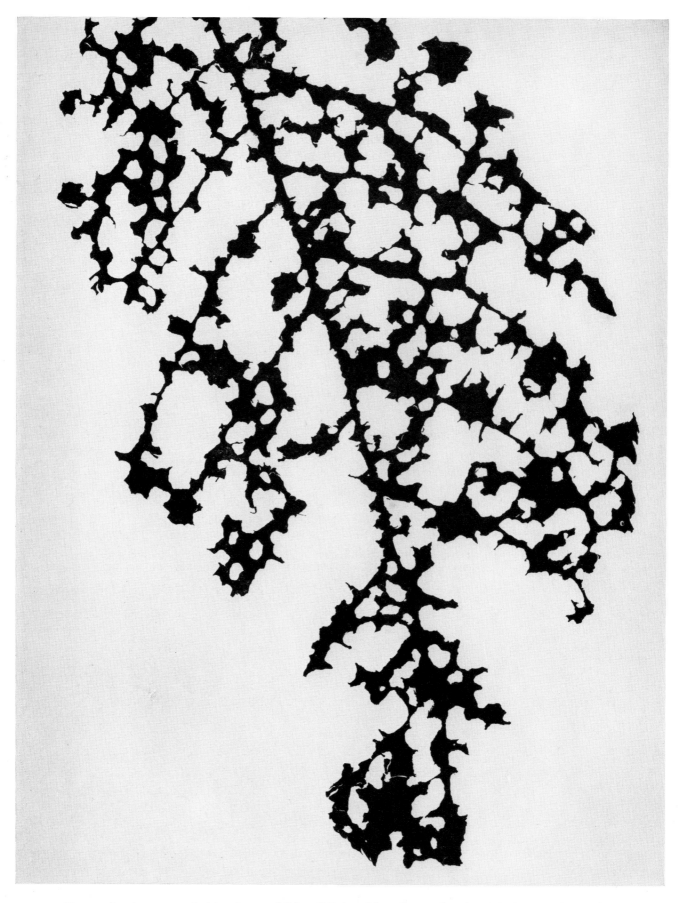

Except for the most primitive forms of life, all living things have a bracing "skeleton"—internal or external—which gives them stability and form. These pictures of a cherry leaf that has been eaten

away by caterpillars and a rotting oak leaf reveal the "skeletons" of leaves—the system of midrib and veins that both stiffen the leafy membrane and supply it with water and minerals.

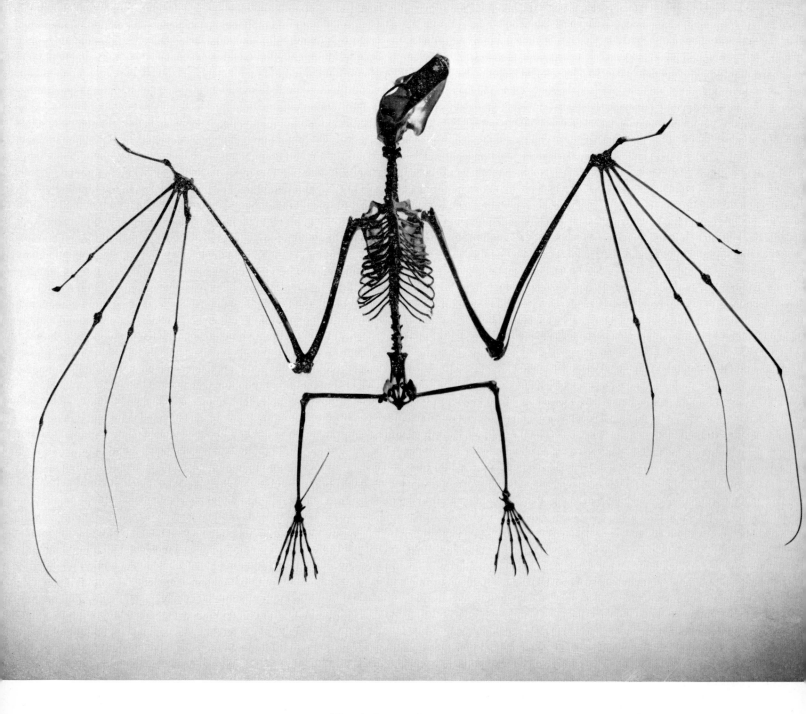

The skeletons of vertebrates are marvels of functional engineering, combining rigidity with flexibility and delicate articulation, maximum strength with minimum weight and expenditure of material. Individual bones are exquisitely sculptural, their beauty that of perfect functional form, their functions expressed in their shapes: the bones of flying or rapidly moving animals are light and hollow, those of animals that move more slowly or swim are heavier and more dense.

To such an extent are a vertebrate's habits reflected in the construction of its skeleton that an expert, merely by studying its bones, can accurately deduce its habits, mode and speed of locomotion, the kind of food it eats, and other pertinent characteristics—a fact which enables paleontologists to reconstruct from a few scattered bones and teeth accurate pictures of animals which they have never seen.

Shown here are the skeletons of a bat and a sloth. The bat skeleton resembles a flying machine, is delicate and light, primarily designed to support, stiffen, and articulate the membranous covering of the wings. The skeleton of the sloth, a tree-climbing animal, is perfectly adapted to this animal's habit of hanging head-down from branches.

Each of these three skeletons belonging to a highly specialized animal is admirably adapted to one particular mode of life. Vertebrae joined together with interlocking prongs give the burrowing African Hero shrew (*above*) a backbone structure strong enough to support the weight of heavy animals which might step on it while in its shallow tunnel.

Its powerful shovel-shaped paws and wedge-shaped skull enable the mole (*left*) to tunnel easily through soil.

And its armored tail plate perfectly protects the Pygmy armadillo (*right*) when, pursued by an enemy, it flees head first into its burrow, sealing the opening as effectively as a cork would a bottle.

One hundred and sixty pairs of hinged ribs forming a flattened articulated bony tube protect the soft body of this four-foot Gaboon viper and support the powerful muscles with which it moves and strikes at its prey. Exquisitely shaped in every detail, tapering gracefully toward both ends of the snake, this skeleton is formed to tolerances that no human engineer would dare to specify.

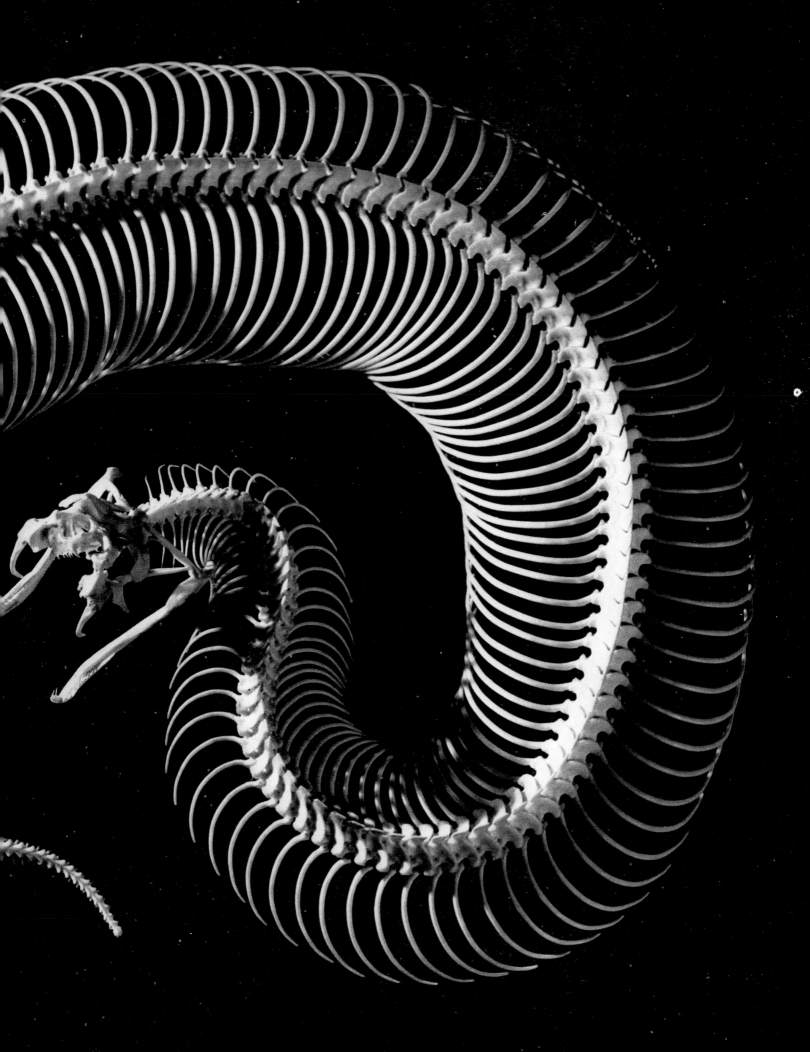

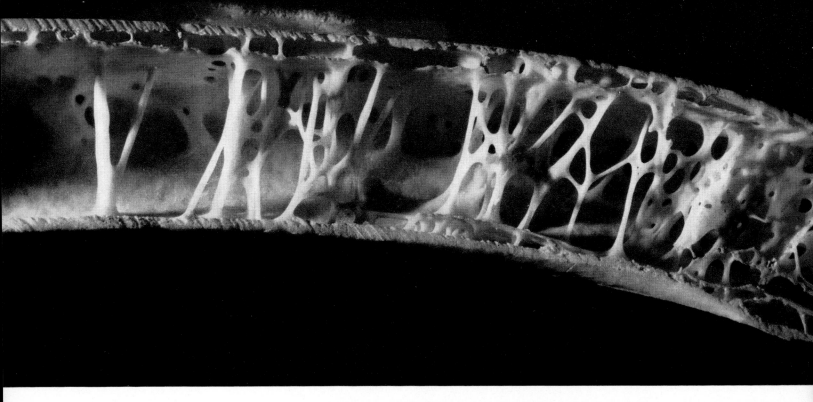

Examples of skeletal engineering. Longitudinal sections of the humerus (upper wing bone) of an eagle—a vertebrate —and the shell of a King crab—a crustacean—show how these structures which belong to completely unrelated animals are stiffened in very similar ways by struts and braces to achieve maximum strength with minimum weight and expenditure of material.

The pelvis of a sloth (*right*), a tree-climbing animal, embodying the principles of the arch to achieve strength and reduce weight through elimination of material in places where it is not needed—the holes in the side plates —is constructed as though it were designed according to the latest engineering theories.

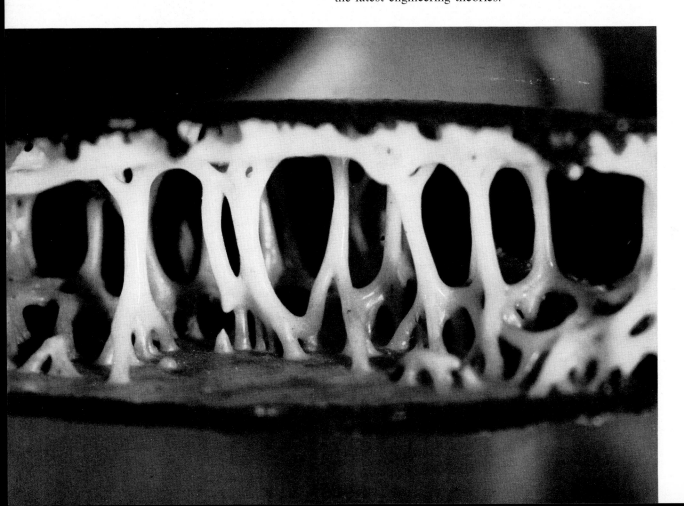

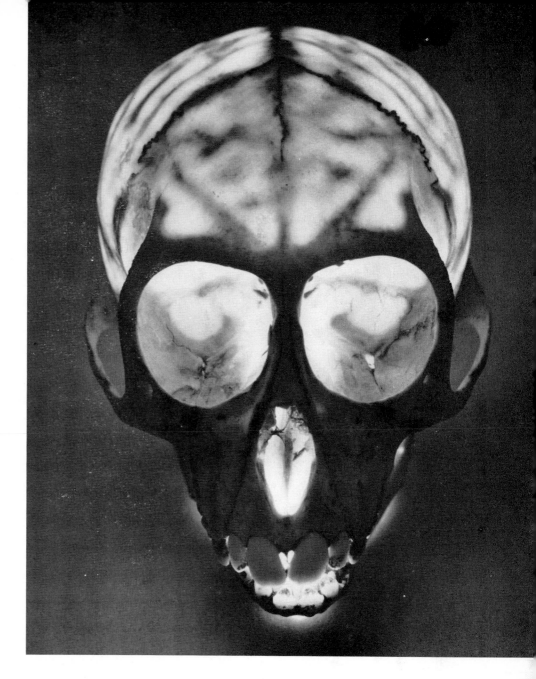

A vertebrate's vital organs are encased in bony armor—
the rib cage shielding the heart and lungs, the skull pro-
tecting the brain. Here too, the structural design ingeniously combines lightness and strength, as evidenced in the
transluminated monkey skull above: strong arched ridges
reinforce the thin bony shell at strategic points, and bracing "beams" strengthen the skull along the lines of junc-
ture of the plates.

87

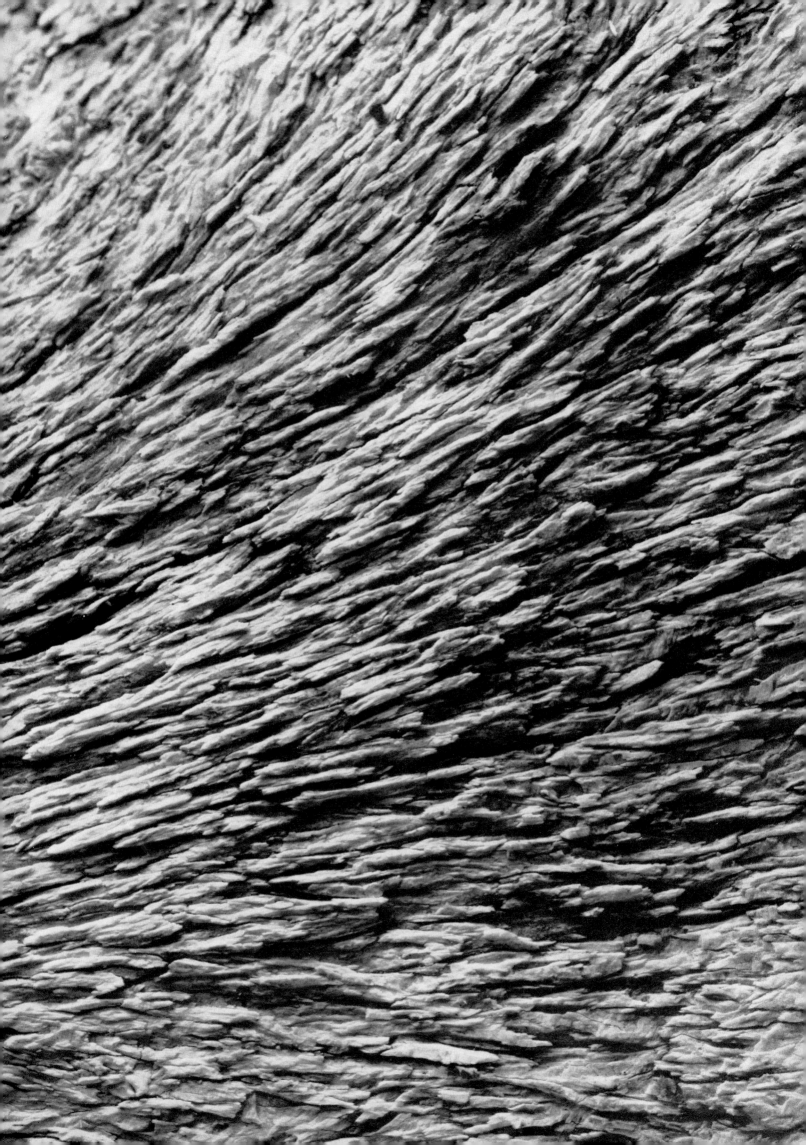

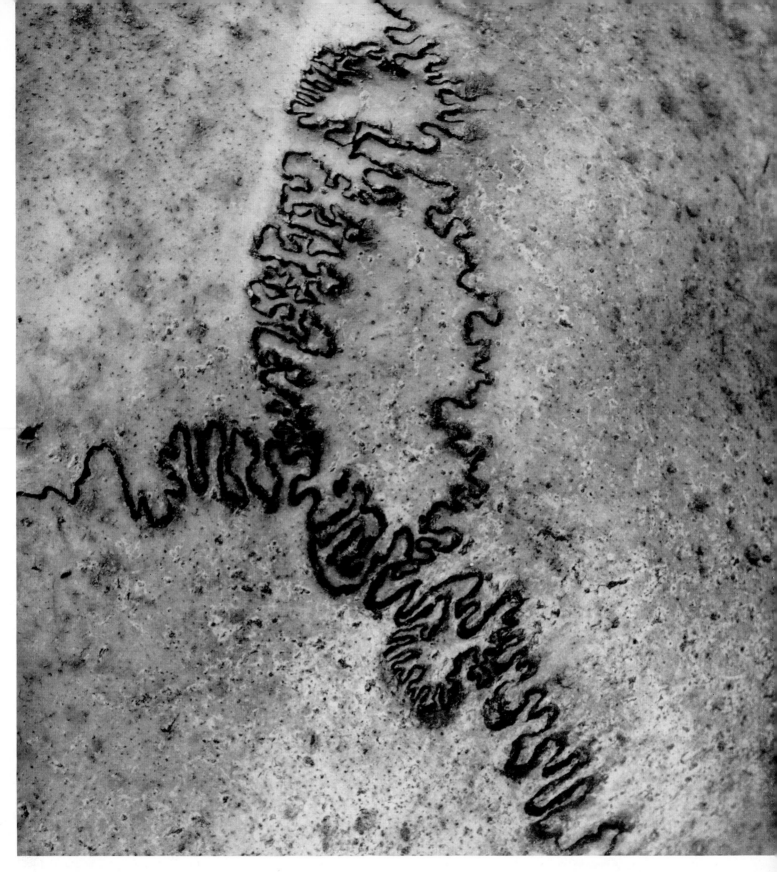

Close-up of the sutures of a human skull shows how an intricate interlocking construction dovetails plate to plate.

Close-up of the weathered jawbone of a cow, magnified six times linear, shows the structural texture of this bone.

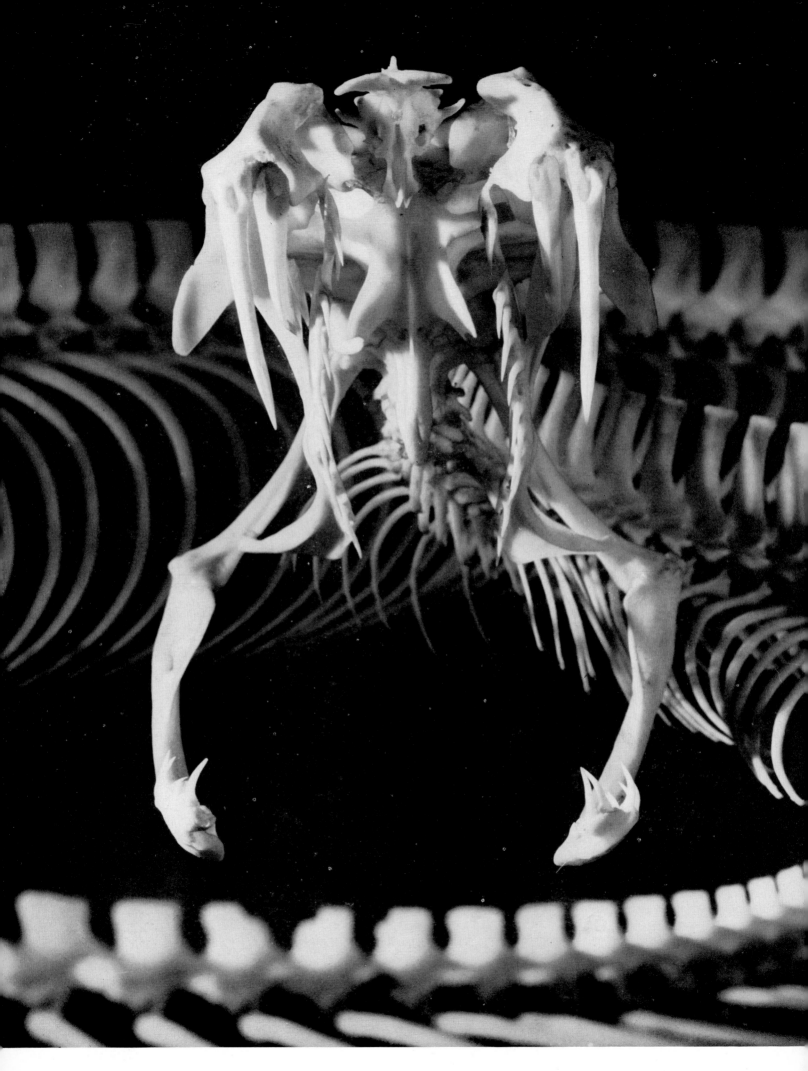

Skull of a Gaboon viper. Its exquisite precision workman-
ship calls to mind fine surgical instruments.

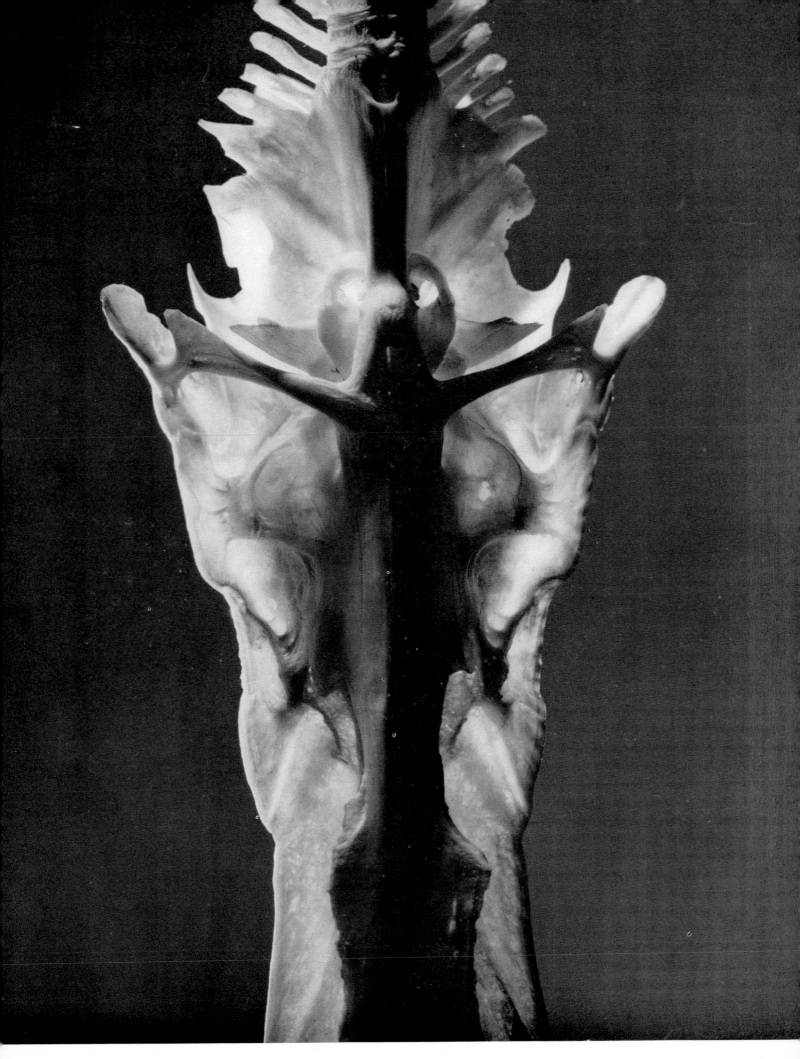

Skull of the Crucifix catfish. Heavy reinforcing ridges
 and braces forming a cross gave the fish its name.

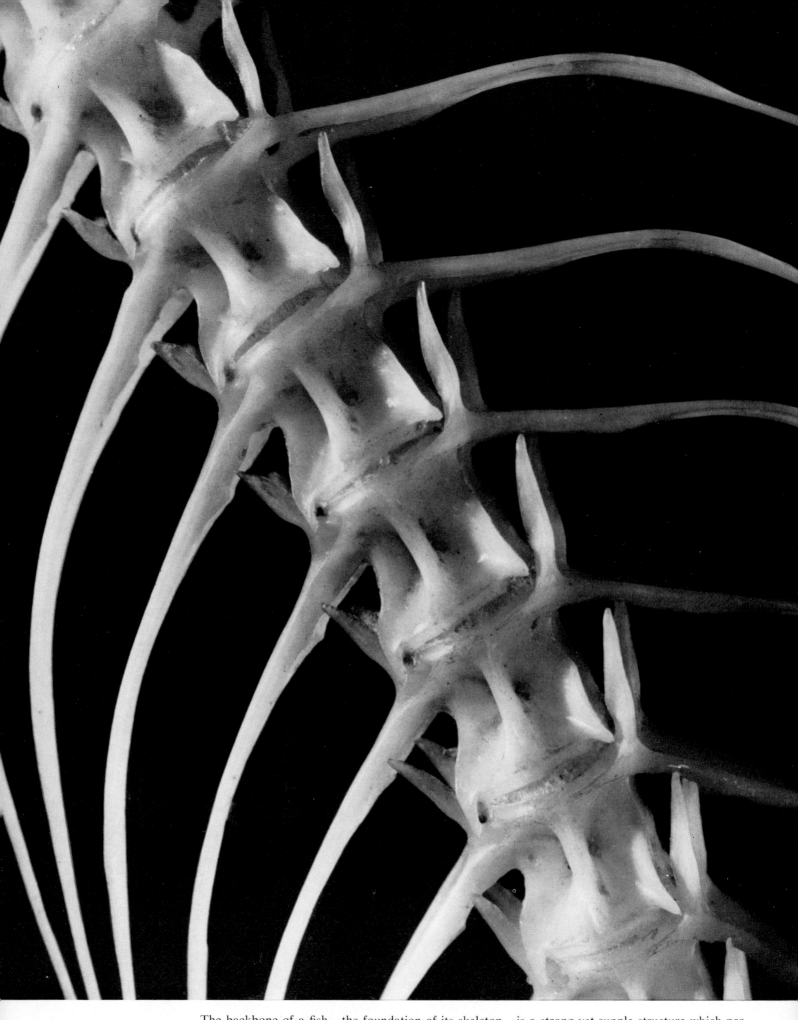

The backbone of a fish—the foundation of its skeleton—is a strong yet supple structure which protects the spinal cord and supports the great locomotor muscles.

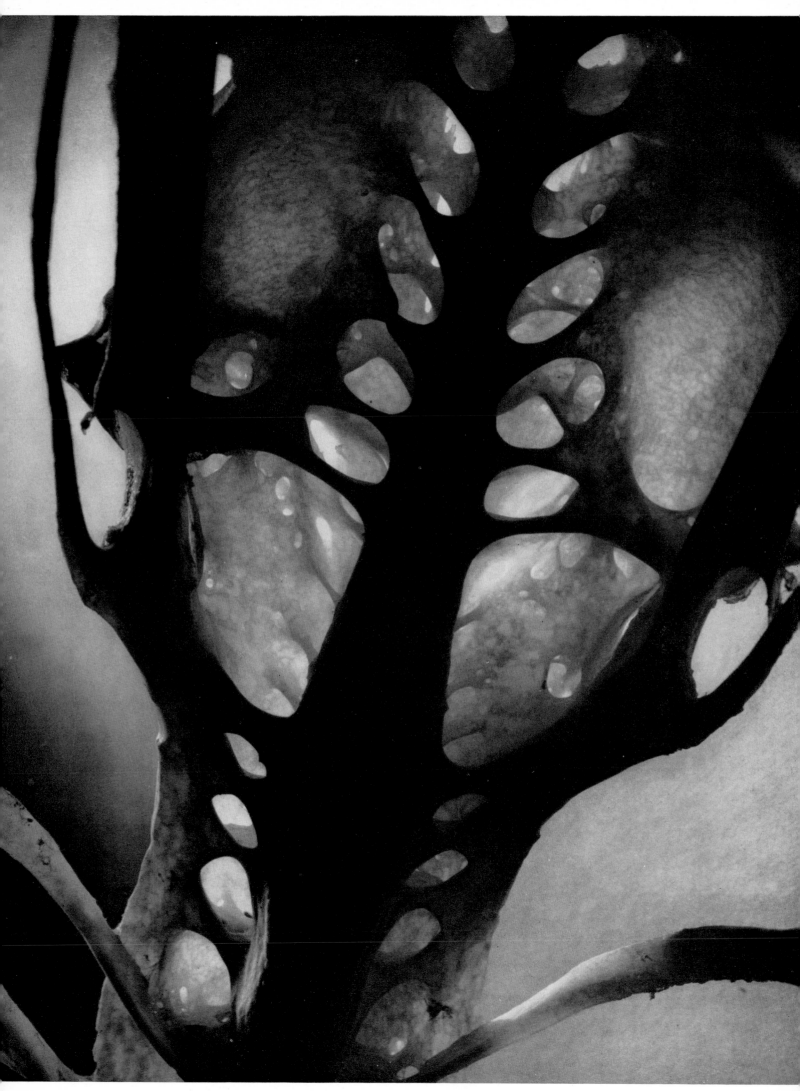

The pelvic girdle of a bird, a thin shell-like structure reinforced by the fused bones of the spine and braced by struts like the keel of a ship for utmost rigidity, is featherlight yet extremely strong.

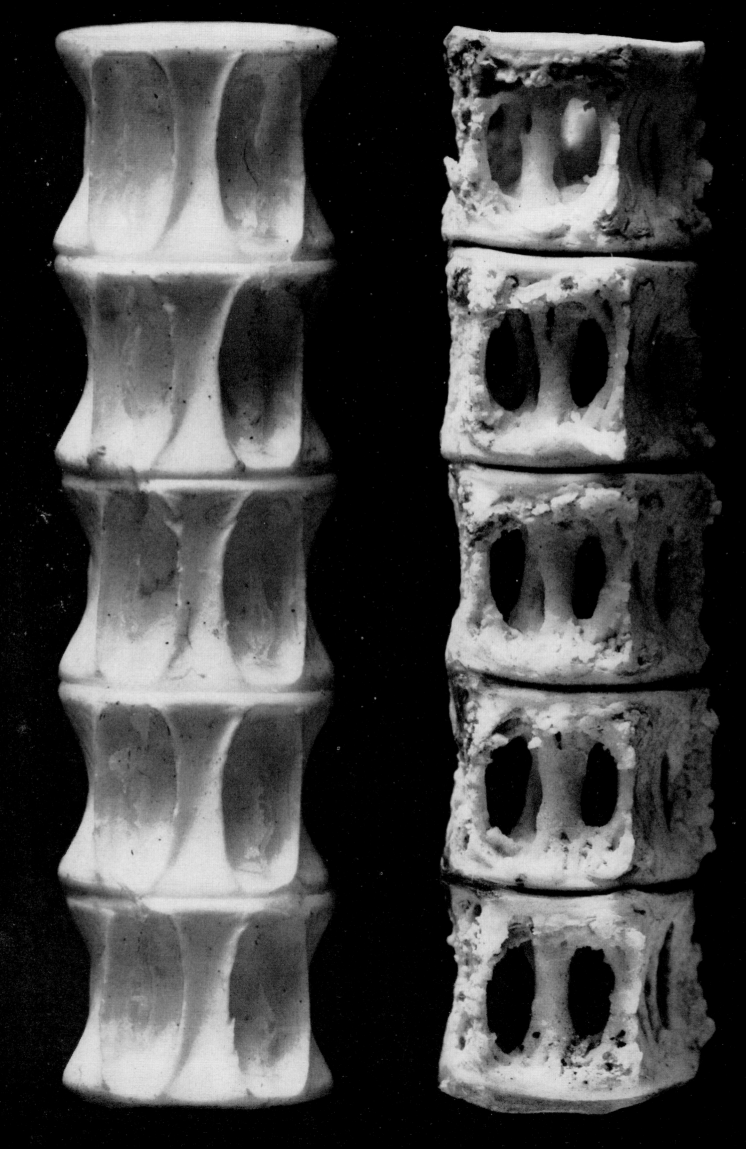

This formidable apparatus, hinged and tooth-studded like a bear trap, is the skeleton of the jaws of an Anglerfish, washed up on the beach near Montauk Point, L.I. Its daggerlike rootless teeth tear away easily at their base, but, like the heads of the mythical Hydra, are steadily replaced by new ones growing up.

Shown here enlarged approximately fifteen times linear
are the teeth of an Anglerfish (*above*) and a skate (*left*).
These teeth do not grow out of the jawbone like human
or mammal teeth, but spring from, and are attached to,
the tough skin which covers the gums of the fish.

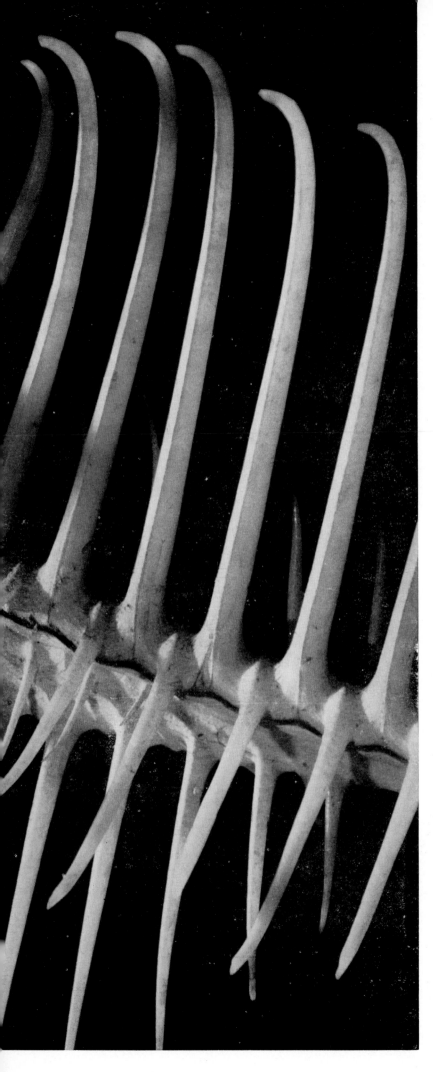

The protective "teeth" of a marine snail. Defensive mechanisms based upon needle-pointed spines are employed by both plants and animals, showing that, despite differences of material and construction, elementary principles of function are essentially alike throughout nature. This, of course, applies also to the principle of the "skeleton"— the bracing frame of an animal or plant. But whereas the skeleton of plants (the woody substance surrounded by the layers of cambium and bark) and vertebrates (the bones) are internal, those of insects, mollusks, coral, etc., are external, not only supporting the soft parts of those animals but also encasing them within a shell of protective armor. And as experts can deduce the habits of a vertebrate from the construction of its bones, so they can draw valid conclusions in regard to habits of mollusks by studying their shells.

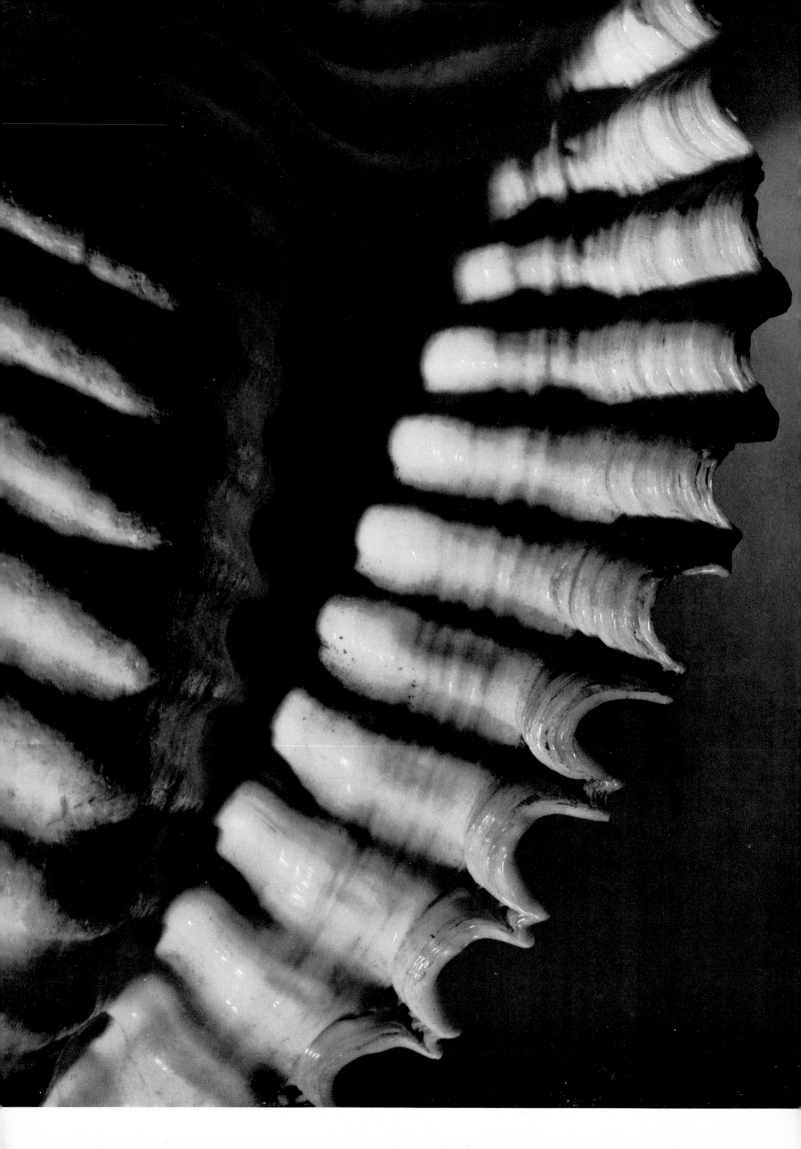

It is a thought-provoking fact that many marine shells suggest or repeat forms typical of the sea. The lip of the shell shown on the facing page, for instance, corrugated for greater stiffness, resembles in design the dorsal fin of a fish. Plumes of foam and spray cast skyward by breaking combers are suggested by the shell shown above. Icebergs drifting in polar seas come to mind in looking at the design of the shell below. And the spirals of the shells on the two following pages repeat the eddy, the surge of swirling waters.

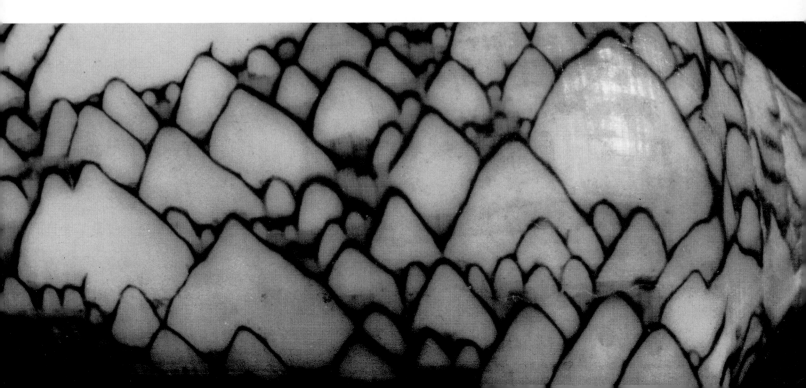

Whereas basically the design of vertebrates (mammals, birds, reptiles, am-
phibians, and fish) and arthropods (insects, spiders, centipedes, lobsters, crabs,
etc.) is always symmetrical, the design of
mollusks is either *more or less* symmetrical, or entirely asymmetrical following
a spiral pattern, like that of the marine
snails shown on the preceding pages or
of the nautilus shown in cross section at
right. As such mollusks grow and their
shells become inadequate, they add in-
creasingly larger sections to the open end,
coiling themselves and their protective
"skeleton" around the axis of a helix.

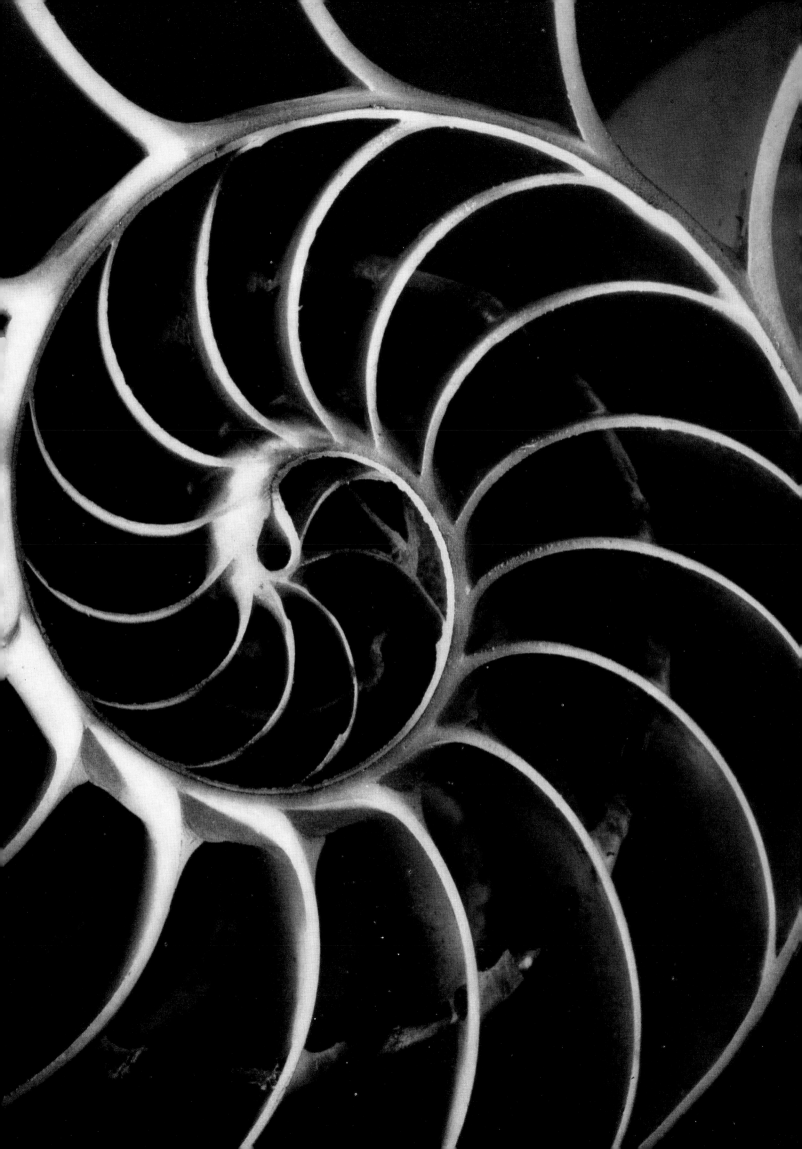

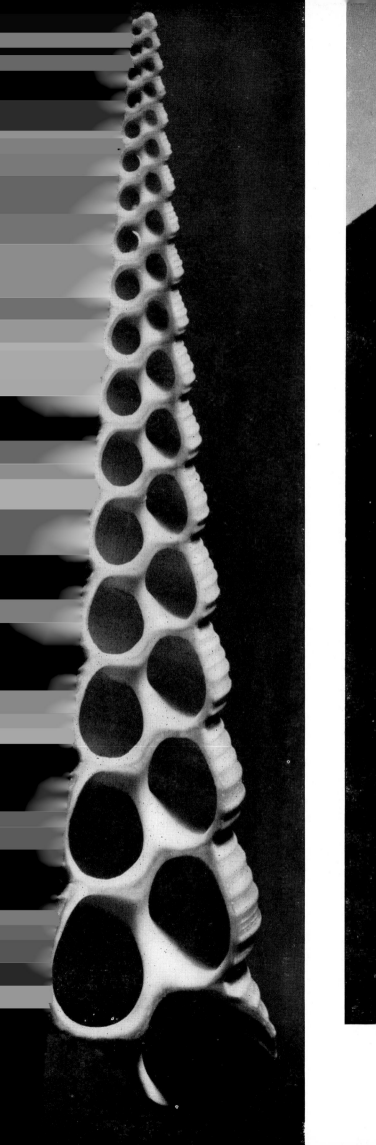

Sectionalization of two marine snails reveals their shells' interiors. To increase its hold on its protective skeleton, the snail above possesses a particularly pronounced inner helix (columella) which considerably increases the contact surface with its shell.

A bryozoan colony (*above*) and the egg capsules of a whelk, a marine snail. Both are common along the New England coast. Each tiny unit contains a life. In the arrangement of its molecules, the gelatinous content of each egg carries the plan for the future snail, complete to the last detail of the whorl. But although millions upon millions of snail eggs are laid each year, most of the hatchlings perish at an early stage of development. Only enough survive to maintain the snail population at a level that is in balance with its environment.

The abundance of the more primitive forms of life staggers the imagination. Since such life-forms are usually quite defenseless--unarmed, nonpoisonous, and not protected by camouflage—losses inflicted upon them by their natural enemies are enormous and must be balanced by an extremely high rate of reproduction.

First of these pictures shows marine snails living on sea-weed, the other, mussels clinging to a rock. If one looks at these closely, one discovers smaller animals among the larger, tiny ones among the smaller, and minute ones next to these—and still there are many more too small to be immediately visible to the eye. Yet these pictures record only a few square inches of a beach many miles long.

Upper surface of the calcareous skeleton of a sand dollar (*left*) and the underside of a starfish skeleton (*right*) consisting of a network of articulated joined calcareous plates, some of which have calcareous spines. Although the design of these animals is radial-symmetrical, it is believed

that they derived from bilateral ancestors and in the course of evolution acquired their circular shape because such a form is more suited to the sedentary habits of these creatures which must constantly be prepared to meet environmental threats to their safety on all sides.

The calcareous external skeleton of a coral magnified fifteen times linear (*left*) and a close-up of the cells of a comb from a hornet nest (*above*). Although the first is secreted by the body of the animal itself (as is the shell of a snail) and the second is constructed from foreign matter (wood pulp), both are organized according to the same geometrical design—circles tightly fitted together and squeezed into the space-saving, more economical form of the hexagon. And both are structures designed primarily for protection—the coral to protect the colony of polyps from animal enemies, and the comb to shield the eggs and larvae of the hornet from rain, cold, and heat.

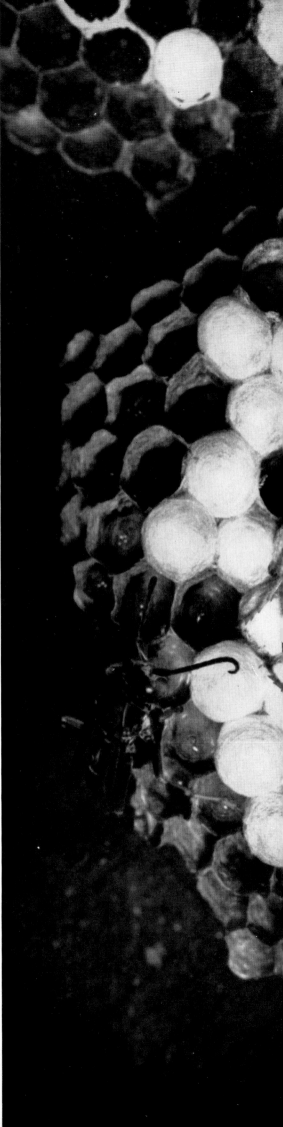

Man is not the world's only architect or engineer. Many animals also build elaborate structures—the dams and flood-control projects of the beaver, the often unbelievably skillfully built nests of birds, the underground labyrinths of the mole, the towering cities of ants and tropical termites, the intricate hanging nests of wasps, the webs and snares of spiders. Some of these are constructed from available materials. Others are made from materials fabricated by the builder itself, which often possess remarkable properties. For example, the nests of the bald-faced hornet (*above*) and the paper wasp (*right*) are built from a paperlike substance made by these insects from wood which they chew and mix with their saliva. The heat-insulating properties of the 1¾″-thick walls of the hornet nest above, as established by scientific measurement (*see p. 158*), is equivalent to that of a brick wall sixteen inches thick. But whereas one cubic inch of brick masonry weighs 27.1 grams, the equivalent volume of this hornet nest's wall material weighs only 0.2 grams.

In sheltered places, the mud dauber wasp builds its herringbone-patterned tubes (*left*) which, subdivided into cells, are the depository for its eggs. Each ridge represents a tiny ball of soft mud which the wasp gathered and carefully patted into place, instinctively guided by "rules" which are as strict as those followed by a master bricklayer.

Carpenter ants carve their nests in the heart wood of timber (*above*), often weakening man-made structures to the point of collapse. Their intricately chambered galleries, resembling in design abstract modern sculpture, are constructed as though they understood the structural properties of wood which they hollow out in a way designed to least weaken it.

Ants are among the most widely spread, successful, and socially developed insects. Their great cities contain from forty thousand to half a million inhabitants, depending on from one to six queens. The mounds, which may reach five to six feet in height and at the base ten to twelve feet in diameter, are constructed of twigs, pine needles, lumps of clay and soil, and are thatched and drained to keep the inside dry under all weather conditions. The picture above shows an ant hill in Colorado, surrounded by a zone which these ants keep bare of vegetation. At right is a cross section of an ant hill in Pennsylvania.

The circular, precision-drilled holes shown at left are the work of mollusks known as "shipworms," a type of greatly elongated clam which uses its shell as a drill and annually does great damage to wooden wharf pilings and ships.

And the carvings shown on this page are made by the larvae of bark beetles which live in the cambium layer of woody plants—the section that lies between the wood and the bark—doing great damage to trees.

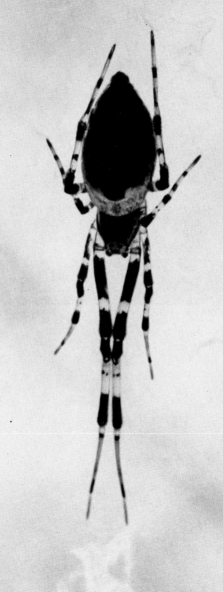

This spider (*Uloborus geniculatus Olivier*), seemingly suspended in mid-air, is poised in a web so fine that it is nearly invisible. And on the facing page, minute drops of dew outline the almost invisible strands of an orb weaver's web. Spiders can at will spin threads that are slick or sticky and of different thicknesses for specific purposes which in regard to tensile strength are stronger than structural steel.

Each kind of spider spins its web in accordance with the design that is typical for its species, instinctively repeating the characteristic pattern as slavishly as if each were working from the same blueprint. At left is a typical orb web (made by the common garden spider); above is the funnel-shaped web of a grass spider (*Agelenopsis*).

The only creatures besides spiders that can to any extent produce silk are the caterpillars, the larvae of butterflies and moths. Photographed in sun and in fog, this is the summer home of the webworm, a relative of the tent caterpillar which spins its nest in spring. Although it appears flimsy and loosely woven, this house of silk is strong enough to protect its inhabitants from caterpillar-eating birds and tight enough to keep out the rain.

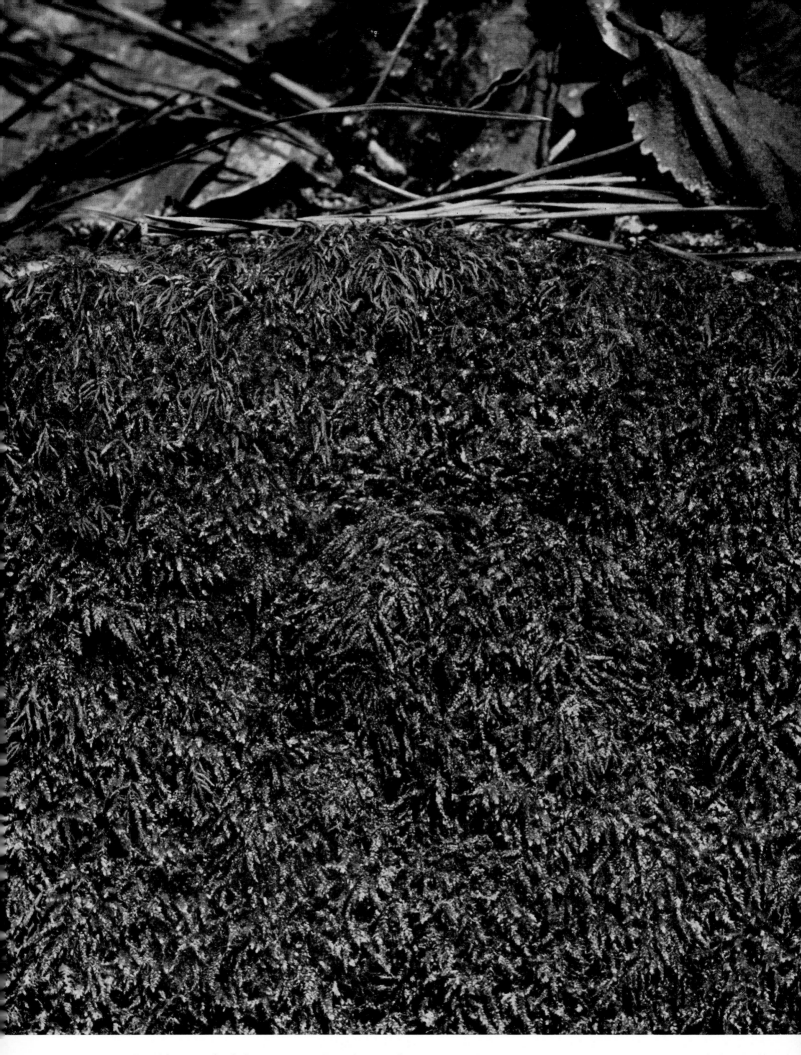

Not all spiders catch their prey in webs. The trapdoor spiders, for example, make silk-lined tubes in the soil 134 which they close with a silk-hinged, camouflaged trapdoor. Peeking out from beneath the partly raised door, the spider patiently waits for its prey. When a suitable victim approaches within striking range, the spider pounces,

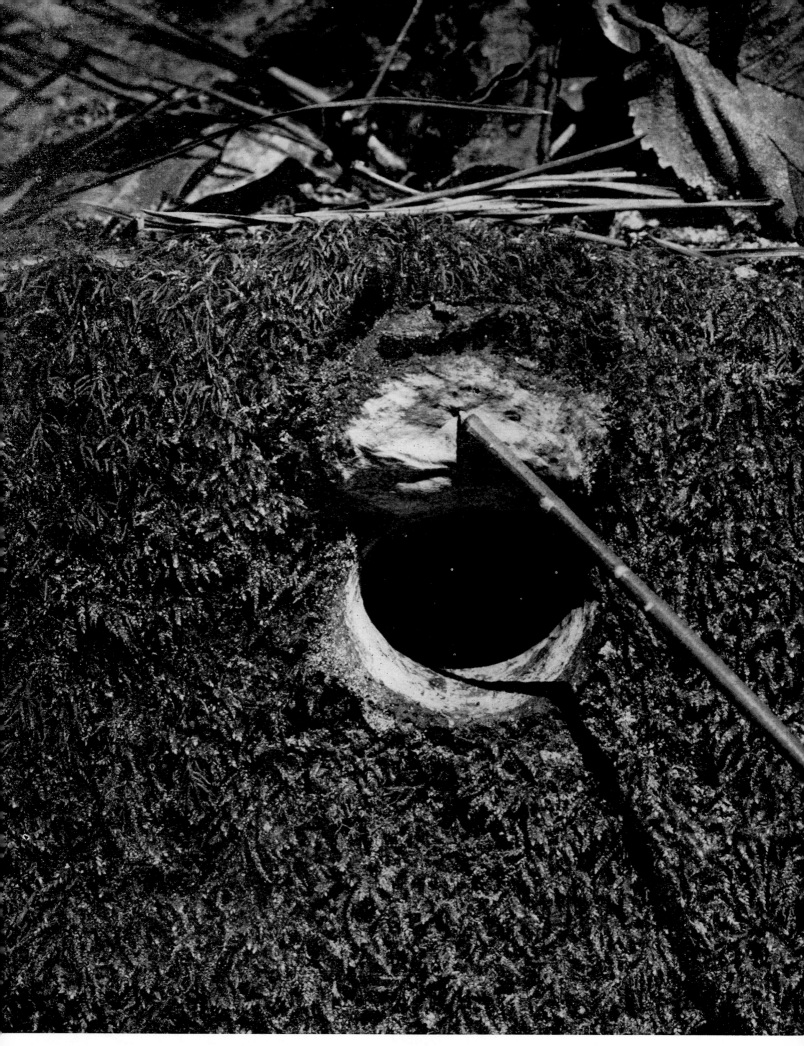

usually keeping part of its body in the doorway to hold the trapdoor open in case a hasty retreat is necessary.

The two photographs above show the identical area of the moss-covered bank of a ditch in Florida. The picture at the left shows the trapdoor shut and that at right shows the trapdoor held open by a stick. This is a perfect example of camouflage instinctively used by an animal.

135

This is the rear view of one kind of trapdoor spider (*Cyclocosmia truncata,* a native of Florida). Like the Pygmy armadillo with its bony tail plate (*p. 81*), this spider also possesses a special rear armor, a defensive shield consisting of horny chitin strong enough to discourage any insect enemy that might attempt to pursue the spider into its burrow. The photograph above shows the spider at the end of its underground retreat, its tail plate tightly corking the tube. This tail plate, with its facelike design, resembles symbolic Aztec representations of the sun.

Spiders take excellent care of their progeny. Although many female spiders do not live to see their young, they guard with their lives the silken sack in which they lay their eggs. Above is the picture of a female Wolf spider carrying her young upon her back like a living fur. At right, young garden spiders emerging from their egg sack descend on silken threads to the ground.

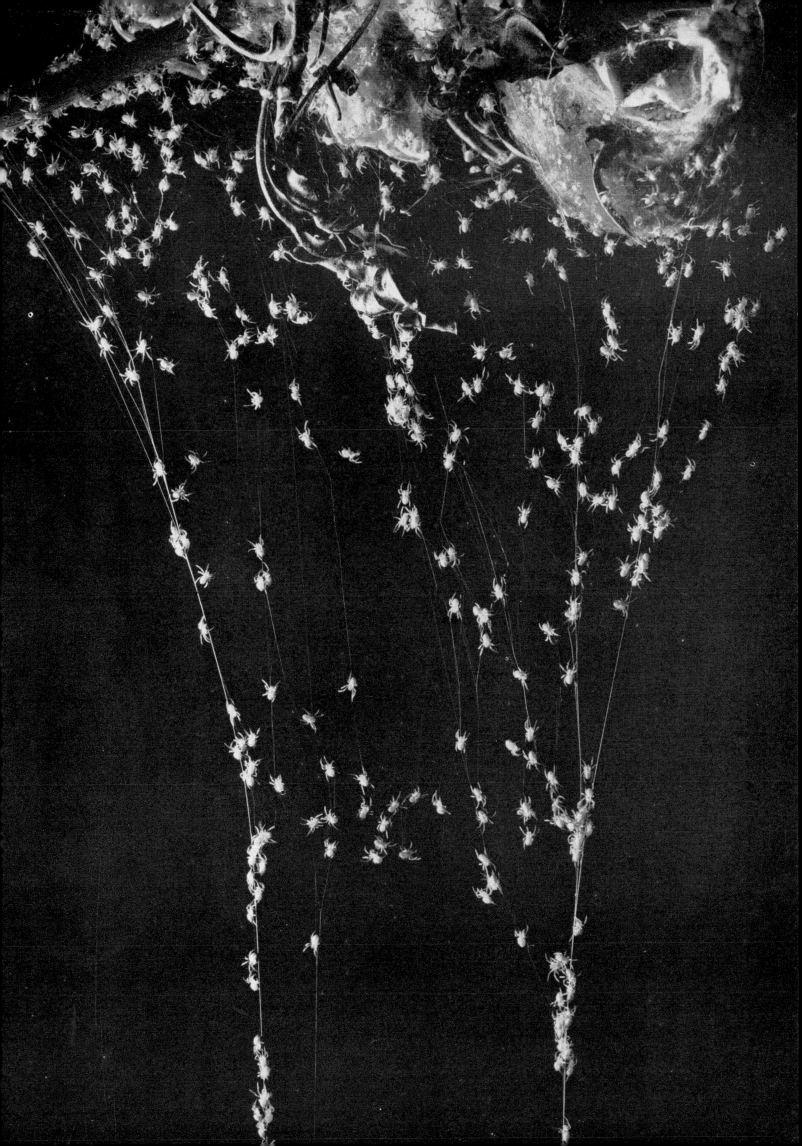

Here are two portraits of beetles. At left, like a knight clad in black shiny armor, foreshadowing in the detail of its construction tank turrets and ball-and-socket joints, is a carnivorous ground beetle, its powerful tonglike man- dibles a menace to any creature weaker than itself. Above, big-eyed, furry, and as complacent-looking as a calf, is a wood-boring beetle, as inoffensive as it appears.

The eyes of arthropods—insects, spiders, centipedes, crabs, etc.—are constructed differently from those of the vertebrates, another example of nature solving *one* problem (vision) in *several* ways. But even among arthropods, eye construction varies according to the needs of the animal. Some, like the caterpillars (*p. 146*), being sluggish plant eaters, have no need for sharp vision and their eyes are little better than light-sensitive pimples. Others,

like the robber fly whose head is shown at right, being hunters which catch their insect prey in flight, have relatively immense "compound eyes" which give their owner remarkable vision of close to 360°.

Above is a close-up of a very primitive eye, that of a King crab, a "living fossil" that through millions of years has hardly changed from the earliest known representatives of its group.

Lump-nosed bat.

The limestone cave near New Braunfels in Texas whose entrance is shown at right is the home of some eight million bats who sleep during the day in its quarter-mile-long interior. As night comes, the bats emerge, first one, then another; then a small band appears in the sunken entrance of the cave. They swirl in circles that swell to tens of thousands, to millions of small chattering, winging forms that quickly fill the shallow bowl in front of the cave like a storm of black snow roaring in wild drafts as each bat, as if riding an immense carousel, swings around in three circles and flies away.

As the sun sets, the creatures of day go to sleep and the creatures of the night begin to awaken. Overhead, like a long plume of smoke, bats fly swampward in search of food. Day and night, from birth to death, life flows in a timeless cycle—life in the soil, water, and air; life of the animal and plant; life of man and the earth, always in constant change and growth so that in all of nature no thing is the same at day's end as it was at day's beginning.

This picture shows the author making the photograph shown on pp. 144-145. See p. 165 for detailed description of the equipment which he used.

The Facts Behind the Pictures

THE VALUE OF A PHOTOGRAPH, measured in terms of accomplishment on the part of the photographer, must, in my opinion, be considered in relation to the amount of information, stimulation, and aesthetic pleasure which it offers to the observer. Some people, of course, are not interested in rocks or insects, for example, and consequently may find photographs of such subjects dull. So I should probably add that, in order to qualify as a judge of its merits, the observer of a photograph must be interested in the subject which it depicts.

This requirement fulfilled, he will find that photographs belong to one of three categories:

1. Pictures that show *less* than one would be able to see if directly confronted with the subject. For example, photographed in black-and-white, colorful flowers or butterflies lose so much that the pictures are most inadequate representations. They fail to show one of the subject's most important features.

2. Black-and-white pictures that convey approxi-

Determination of the insulation value of a hornet nest's wall in comparison to brick masonry. See pp. 120-121.

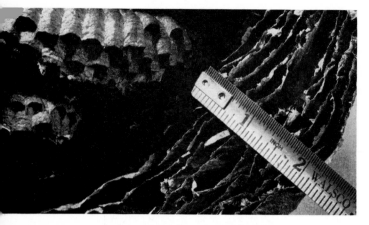

Cross section of the wall of a hornet nest which shows the insulating air spaces between the layers of "paper" manufactured by the insects from wood.

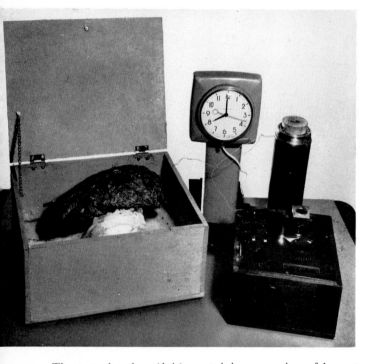

The test chamber (*left*) containing a section of hornet nest wall with thermocouple attached to its outer shell. A 15-watt light bulb served as constant heat source. Temperature measurements were obtained with a Leeds-Northrup potentiometer (*right*) at five-minute intervals over a period of sixty minutes.

Visual evaluation of the test. The insulation value of the tested section of hornet nest wall (*left*) is equivalent to that of a brick wall sixteen inches thick (*right*). Since brick masonry weighs approximately 27.1 grams per cubic inch in contrast to the 0.2 grams for the hornet nest wall, brick masonry only 0.013″ thick (*center*) would weigh as much as one thickness of hornet nest wall (*left*).

mately *the same impression* as that created by the subject itself. (In most instances, through skillful use of the photographic medium, a photographer can "symbolize" color as well as three-dimensionality and motion in terms of graphic black-and-white.) Record shots and the majority of photo-illustrations fall into this second category. They are highly useful and adequate for many purposes, but such photographs are rarely stimulating because they tell nothing new to an observer who is familiar with the subject.

3. Pictures that show *more* than one would be able to see if directly confronted with the subject. Such photographs are always stimulating because they provide new experience, add to knowledge, or, in one way or another, widen one's intellectual or emotional horizon. I have tried to the best of my ability to document the subjects of this book with photographs of this category.

One reason that a photograph can show more is that our range of vision is limited, whereas that of the camera is not. Objects that are too small or too far away to be seen clearly can easily be photographed in a scale sufficiently large to make detail apparent. Furthermore, we are confronted on all sides by an overwhelming array of impressions which makes it difficult to pay undivided attention to detail. A photograph, however, isolates a specific subject, permitting an interested observer to study it.

But more important is the fact that *a good photograph shows the subject to best advantage*—at the most typical moment, from the most favorable angle, and in the most suitable light. It is in relation to these factors that the skill—or lack of skill—of a photographer becomes apparent. There are always many different ways of photographing a specific subject. No two photographers will produce identical pictures of the same subject. The photograph of one may be conventional and dull, showing the observer nothing new. That of the other may be informative and stimulating because of a fresh approach, imaginative concept, or unusual pictorial treatment. Imaginatively seen, even the most common and stereotyped subjects can become new and interesting.

Many people believe that in order to make unusual

158

photographs one must have either special equipment or use certain difficult techniques. This is not true. All the pictures in this book were taken with either a Rolleiflex, a Hasselblad single-lens reflex camera, or one of two ordinary 4″x5″ view cameras—equipment used by many amateurs. The film I used was Kodak Super XX, rollfilm in the Rolleiflex and Hasselblad, filmpack in the 4x5's. These were developed in Kodak developers DK-20 and D-76, respectively, and printed on Kodabromide paper. To improve contrast and tone separation I occasionally used a color filter. All my exposures were determined with the aid of a Weston II exposure meter.

The difference between average and unusual photographs is not based upon differences in equipment and technique, but upon subject selection, approach, and treatment—differences in "seeing."

To begin with, I avoided photographing subjects that were not suitable for black-and-white. This, of course, excluded all subjects whose most important feature is color, and those which have neither sharply defined forms nor sufficient contrast between light and dark. I also avoided subjects which present a confusion of detail and form, and most overall shots and wide-open views which, though pleasing to the eye, usually appear disappointing in photographs.

Next to discrimination in subject selection, perhaps the most important prerequisite for making interesting photographs is the photographer's ability to "edit" pictures *before* he takes them. This means paying special attention to such factors as perspective and distortion; determination of that angle of view which, by emphasizing typical qualities, shows the subject to best advantage; never allowing the background to detract from the subject proper or to blend or otherwise interfere with its outline and form; and being sure that the illumination strikes the subject from an angle which insures good surface texture rendition and black-and-white contrast. It is this "editing" which enables a photographer to leave a much stronger impression than the actual subject under ordinary conditions. Such intensification can make us consciously aware of the nature of our surroundings.

Determination of the tensile strength of the strands of a spider web in comparison to structural steel. See p. 128.

Five strands of spider webbing (*right*), mounted parallel on a frame under uniform tension in the jaws of a Scott Inclined Plane Tester of 0 to 250 grams capacity, were broken at a constant rate of loading. The tension necessary to cause rupture was automatically recorded on graph paper.

Visual evaluation of the test. The number of individual filaments per strand was counted under a microscope and their average diameter determined. From the results of the above test the tensile strength in pounds per square inch was then calculated for comparison to tabled figures for structural steel. The difference in the value of the figures representing the tensile strength of spider silk and structural steel is visually expressed in the difference in length of the two weights shown above.

The author making the photograph shown on p. 115. A surprisingly large number of interesting objects of nature can be photographed successfully with comparatively simple equipment such as this Rolleiflex in conjunction with a set of slip-on lenses.

People often ask me how I photograph certain subjects, what kind of equipment I use, and what "tricks" I resort to when I take extreme close-ups of subjects such as live insects or spiders whose images are shown several times life-size on the film. Here are some answers to these questions:

So that he may be prepared for most eventualities, a naturalist should have two different types of camera: a 4"x5" view-type camera, and a small-size roll-film reflex camera.

The 4x5 is ideal for photographing inanimate subjects and plants—anything from landscapes down to close-ups of flowers, shells, spider webs, etc. A photographer should take advantage of the immobility of such subjects and use the large, although somewhat cumbersome view camera because it offers unique advantages for this kind of work: its "swings" (front and back adjustments) often make it possible to extend the zone of sharpness in depth to distances that are impossible to cover sharply merely by stopping down the lens. This enables the photographer to produce effects which he could not produce with any other type of camera. Interchangeability of lenses makes a view camera equally suitable for photographing a distant mountain range (with a long-focus lens) or the whorl in the shell of a tiny snail (with a short-focus lens). Lenses for view cameras are, as a rule, considerably less ex-

pensive than comparable lenses for cameras of the Leica or Hasselblad type, particularly if the photographer is wise enough to choose the old-fashioned, relatively slow (f/6.3) but extremely sharp lenses of the pre-war Tessar and Dagor type. For close-ups, fast lenses offer no advantage over slow lenses since, in order to produce sufficient sharpness in depth, the photographer must take his pictures with the lens considerably stopped down. Furthermore, view cameras offer the unique advantage of rear-focusing—the best method of quickly and accurately bringing very close subjects (rendition in near-natural size or larger) into focus without repeated annoying and time-consuming readjustments of distance between subject and camera. And finally, the larger negative size of the 4x5 removes worry about film grain, makes for relatively easy processing with full utilization of inherent film speed, and makes it possible to produce prints which are unsurpassed in sharpness, crispness of contrast, and definition of fine detail.

The small-size rollfilm reflex camera is ideal for photographing animals—anything from birds to bugs. This camera can be either a 35 mm (Leica with reflex housing, or a true reflex camera such as the Pentacon), or a 2¼"x2¼" reflex (Rolleiflex, if necessary in conjunction with slip-on lenses for close-up photography; or one of the more versatile single-lens reflex cameras such as the Hasselblad,

This picture shows how the photograph on p. 100 was made. Held in position by the C-clamp, only the center part of the jaw of a skate was photographed.

Master Reflex, Reflex Korelle, etc.). The Rolleiflex, which also is an excellent all-round camera for general nature photography, has, like all twin-lens reflex cameras, the disadvantage of limited bellows extension which precludes photographing very small subjects in sufficiently large scale. However, it has the advantage over single-lens reflex cameras of presenting a groundglass image which is always bright no matter how far the taking lens is stopped down, which, of course, considerably facilitates focusing. On the other hand, cameras of the single-lens reflex type in conjunction with extension tubes or auxiliary bellows permit the photographer to take close-ups in any desired scale. Because of these different advantages, I use both a Rolleiflex and a Hasselblad.

The main advantage of a reflex-type camera is speed of operation: the groundglass image is visible until the very moment of exposure (in twin-lens reflex cameras also during and after exposure) since no image-blocking film holder has to be inserted between the groundglass and the lens as in view-type cameras; film transport and shutter cocking are coupled and operated with the twist of a single knob; large film magazines holding up to thirty-six shots (35 mm cameras), interchangeable rollfilm magazines (Hasselblad), and spring-motor driven rapid-winding devices (35 mm cameras) permit the photographer to shoot whole picture-sequences

within a matter of seconds. In addition, these cameras are relatively small and light, can be carried easily even if for practical reasons weight and bulk must be limited, and negative material for a hundred shots (35 mm) takes less space than a single film pack for a 4x5.

The accessories which I carry are few and simple:

Heading the list is a photoelectric exposure meter (I use a Weston) which, in my opinion, is an absolute necessity. In the field, a naturalist constantly finds himself confronted with unique photographic opportunities. But since the most interesting picture possibilities often present themselves when light conditions are poor and difficult to judge by "feeling"—at dawn, in the deep shade, at dusk—it is vitally important that the first exposure be correct since one rarely gets a chance for a repeat shot. This makes a reliable exposure meter indispensable.

If close-ups are to be taken and the available light is too weak to permit hand-held exposures, to make it possible to stop subject motion, or to allow for the use of diaphragm stops small enough to produce sufficient sharpness in depth, auxiliary illumination must be used. I have had excellent results with the Mighty Midget speedlight which I use outdoors on batteries and indoors on AC house current. An accessory for this speedlight which is invaluable for

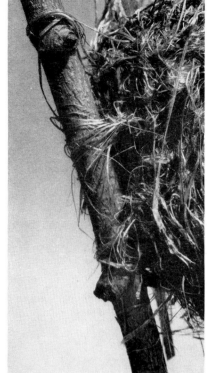

Determination of the amount of weight that an Oriole's nest will support before tearing away from the twigs to which it is attached. (*Left*) Over-all view of the pouch-like nest before the start of the test. (*Right*) Close-up of anchorage to horizontal twig. (*Opposite page*) To prevent the load applied to the nest from snapping the supporting twigs (which had dried and become brittle since the branch had been cut from the tree), the twigs were wired to a supporting backboard and to an upright stay. Furthermore, in order that the lead shot used for the initial loading would not separate the weave of the nest and pour through, a gauze liner was inserted into the nest. A spring scale was then attached to the wire frame of the gauze liner in such a way that it did not register until the nest collapsed (*fourth picture*).

The initial loading was accomplished by funneling six

extreme close-ups is the circular flash tube which can be mounted directly on the front of the lens by means of a threaded adapter ring. Encircling the lens, it provides completely shadowless illumination which is particularly desirable for extreme close-ups in color. It furthermore solves in the simplest way the otherwise often baffling problem of how adequately to light a subject which is so close to the front of the camera (rendition in natural size or larger) that it cannot be properly illuminated from the side by flash.

If light conditions or demands for particularly great extension of sharpness in depth make hand-held exposures impossible or if a 4x5 is used, the camera must be supported by a tripod. With many of the most interesting subjects close to or on the ground, the tripod must allow for a camera position relatively close to the ground. Unsurpassed for such purposes is the "Stubby" (made by Quick-set in Chicago), an elevator-equipped, strong, yet comparatively light tripod which extends from thirteen to thirty-six inches.

Three other accessories which I consider essential are filters, lens shade, and cable release.

Filters in the colors red and deep red (Wratten A and F), deep yellow (Wratten K3), and blue (Wratten C5) are for control of tone separation and contrast in black-and-white photography. In conjunction with the 4x5 I use gelatine filters which are inexpensive and practical because one filter fits any size lens if attached to it with adhesive tape. Whenever possible, I tape the filter to the back of the lens board.

The lens shade should be as long as possible without blocking out parts of the image. Most commercially available lens shades are too short and hence of little value unless extended with a piece of stiff black paper attached with masking tape. For a 4x5, the "Graphic" bellows-type lens shade (*see photograph on p. 157*) is unsurpassed since it can be attached directly to the front of the camera itself, fits any lens regardless of focal length and diameter, and can be extended sufficiently to be effective even when backlighted close-ups are taken.

A cable release should be used if the camera is mounted on a tripod. Otherwise it is almost impossible to avoid jarring the camera when tripping the shutter—a common cause for pictures which "un-

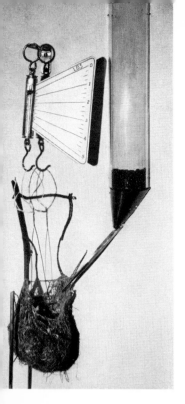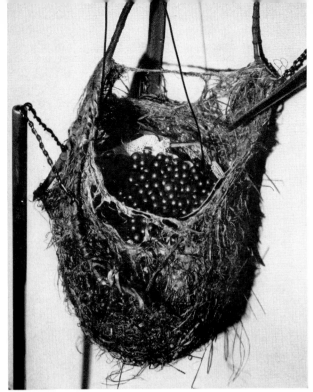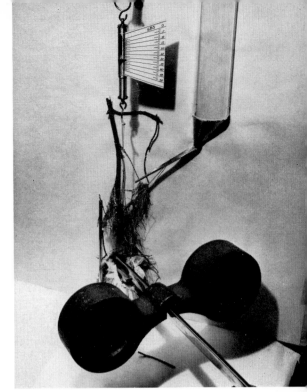

pounds of lead shot into the nest. Since this load did not cause rupture of the anchoring although the entire cavity of the pouch was filled with lead (*fifth picture*), additional load was gradually built up via a calibrated lever arm and sliding weight until rupture occurred (*sixth picture*). At this point the spring scale accepted the load and it was found that the weight necessary to tear the nest from its support was thirty-three pounds.

By measuring the pull on the nest from various angles at a wind velocity of 12.5 miles per hour, a resistance of twenty-three grams was recorded. Based on this figure and the anchoring power of thirty-three pounds, it is estimated that the nest would resist winds of hurricane velocity before tearing from its supports. This strength, of course, is far in excess of the strength of the supporting twigs.

explainably" are not as sharp as the photographer expected them to be.

In addition to this strictly photographic equipment, on field trips I carry a kit containing the following items:

Black masking tape which can be used for dozens of different purposes such as taping a filter to a lens; mending a chafed corner of the camera bellows; extending the lens shade; sealing a container or an exposed filmpack; holding a branch in place for a picture; fastening a cardboard background to a suitable support; etc.

Thin strong fishing line for tying branches to prevent them from moving in and out of focus while the insect, etc., which they support is being photographed.

Strong garden scissors to cut off impedimenta such as weeds and small branches which might block the subject.

A pair of pliers with wire cutters and a couple of small *screw drivers* to build some unanticipated rig or make emergency repairs.

Long industrial tweezers to handle and place in position small fragile objects of nature.

A few glass bottles and *canvas collecting bags* for taking home specimens for identification.

The two most important requirements of a naturalist-photographer are patience and ingenuity. Subjects are more elusive and working conditions less controllable, than those of photographers working in almost any other field. Often, a naturalist rises before dawn, spends all day in the field, not returning until it is too dark to photograph. He gets blistered by sun and drenched by rain. He must be prepared to miss many meals. He must love solitude and wide open spaces, rocks, trees, and the sky. When photographing animals, he may have to spend days or weeks before he gets his first chance at a shot; and then light conditions may be so bad that he gets no picture. When photographing plants, his patience may be severely taxed in waiting for the wind to subside long enough so that he can expose a negative that will be free from blur. When photographing rocks or scenery he may find the light unsuitable upon his arrival and have to wait for hours for the sun to move into a better position, or be forced to return on another day. He encounters much frustration, but he does not mind because he loves his subjects and enjoys the time he spends out of doors,

Determination of the crush-resistance of Hardshell clams (Quahogs).

A hydraulic press, hand-operated to cause breakage within thirty seconds after the start of application of load, was used to break the shell, and an attached pressure gauge was used to measure the force (*left*). Eight different clams approximately three inches across were used for the test, and the average force necessary to break their shells was found to be fifty pounds (minimum forty-five and maximum sixty-six pounds)—equal to the weight of ten large-size bricks (*right*). However, if pressure had been applied, not concentrated upon the extreme points of the shell as in the test, but evenly distributed over the entire area of the shell, loads many times as high as those applied in this test could have been sustained by the clams without damage to their shells.

with the result that he benefits whether or not he is able to make photographs.

As his experience grows, every naturalist-photographer gradually develops certain methods to better his chances for success. Here are some of the things which I learned, either from watching others, from talking with more experienced colleagues, or by accidentally stumbling upon them myself.

One of the greatest obstacles to getting sharp close-ups of insects and plants is wind. Even if speedlight illumination is used to eliminate blur due to motion during exposure, it is still almost impossible to focus accurately upon a branch or stalk which sways back and forth in the breeze. Under such conditions, I use thin fishing line to tie the branch or stalk to some sturdy object—stones, rocks, or sticks driven like tent stakes into the ground. Two, or if necessary three such lines, tied to the branch in such a way that they are outside the picture area, are sufficient to hold it in focus.

Focusing accurately upon a very close animate subject can require so much time that the subject probably will have departed long before the photographer is ready to shoot it. In such cases, I prefocus my reflex camera at a safe distance (so that I don't frighten my subject) by focusing upon another object of similar size (perhaps a leaf) until I get a sharp image in the desired scale on the groundglass. Then, without touching the focusing knob again, I slowly move the whole camera toward the subject until its image appears in sharp focus on the groundglass, at which instant I take the picture with electronic flash.

In photographs, outdoor subjects should never appear as though they were taken with artificial light (even if this were actually the case). For this reason, I avoid the use of cross-light produced by a main side-light and a fill-in light at the camera since criss-crossing shadows are almost unavoidable. Instead, I use a single light source—either a high side-light or the shadowless light produced by the circular flash tube mentioned before. If necessary, side-light is supplemented by totally diffused and hence shadowless light reflected by a piece of white cardboard which serves as shadow fill-in. I found that in close-ups with a depth not exceeding the effective range of the flash such illumination is virtually indistinguishable from sunlight.

The patience of a naturalist would be severely taxed if he attempted to photograph winged insects in their natural outdoor habitat. A relatively easy way to get pictures of such insects is to capture them in a butterfly net and to take them home alive and undamaged. Prepare a natural setting (for example, dig up plants or flowers of the type on which the insect has been observed in nature, plant them in a flower pot, and arrange this setting in front of a suitable background of leaves, grass, stones, or a sky-colored piece of cardboard set far enough away to be outside the range of shadows cast by the plants). Finally, in this setting, *photograph a day insect in a relatively dark room, and a night insect in bright daylight.* It is surprising how often (though not always) even the liveliest day insect can easily be handled and "posed" in dim light, and how docile night insects are in daylight. As long as the setting (plants, grass, flowers, dead leaves, bark, sand, gravel, or rocks) duplicates in detail the conditions under which the insect lives—a task which is usually not difficult to achieve since the area to be photographed is generally only inches wide and deep— pictures of live insects which are neither chilled nor anesthetized, taken in this manner, are not "fakes" but valid documents of nature which can in no way be distinguished from photographs taken outdoors —except that on the average they are better and more informative than pictures taken on location under less favorable conditions.

It is usually not difficult to get typical pictures of nonflying insects, and of caterpillars, spiders, etc., if the photographer uses the right approach which can be summed up in one word: patience. He must avoid fast and sudden movements and be sure not to cast a shadow upon the subject because these frighten the subject so that it runs away or curls up and "plays dead." Often, it is possible to prefocus on a suitable spot and gently prod the subject with a blade of grass until it moves into focus. Such suitable spots are: the entrances of insects' nests and burrows; the tunnel of a ground spider's web (*see p. 131*); certain flowers to which certain insects return again and again (secure the stem with fishing line as previously described to prevent the flower from swaying out of focus); the area on the trunks of trees where sap flows attracting many insects; a colony of aphids tended by ants; the funnel-shaped crater of an ant-lion's trap; etc. A typical set-up of this kind is illustrated by the photograph on p. 157 which shows the author photographing a wolf spider feeding on a grasshopper (*see pp. 144-145*). Once a spider has started to feed it is reluctant to

relinquish its prey and can be photographed easily. In this particular case, the following details of the camera set-up should be noted:

The tripod, a Quick-set Senior, was so high that the camera could not be mounted close enough to the ground. To overcome this, the elevator post was reversed and the camera mounted upside-down beneath the tripod. In order to gain additional sharpness in depth the swing back of the view camera was tilted forward—notice that it is no longer parallel to the camera front. To prevent vibration, which is an ever-present danger particularly when the bellows are fully extended, the front of the camera bed was secured to a tripod leg with adhesive tape; in this way, the camera was held in place both front and back. Because the sky was overcast and the illumination poor, to improve contrast and definition, the picture was taken with flash. Notice that the flash gun and the flash lamp rig are attached to the tripod head in such a way that they swing with the camera, thus throwing the light exactly upon the area on which the lens is focused. This rig was made from parts of a discarded desk lamp. It is light, flexible, and enables the photographer to direct the light to any desired spot. Notice, furthermore, the "Graphic" bellows-type lens shade which effectively prevents the backlight flash from striking the lens, and the cable release which prevents jarring the camera when making the exposure.

Whether or not a naturalist-photographer is able to get a good picture of a particular subject is often dependent upon his resourcefulness and inventiveness. The webs of orb spiders, for example, are exquisitely beautiful, but their threads are so fine that they either do not show at all in a photograph, or show only in those few areas where the light happens to strike them at just the right angle. Of course, all spider webs photograph beautifully on misty mornings when they are picked out by dew. But a naturalist cannot always rely upon finding them so. Instead, he uses a small atomizer of water with which he blows a mist upon the web. The effect is very similar to that of nature's own dew.

How does one take a close-up of a biting mosquito? It is easily done if one catches some mosquitoes and starves them for a few days. Then, one puts a mosquito into a test tube; gets a helper-victim; holds the test tube with its opening against his arm; focuses upon the tiny area of skin inside the test tube; waits until the hungry mosquito alights and begins to feed; slowly removes the test tube; makes final adjustments of focus; and takes the picture with flash.

Any photographer should know that, when taking close-ups, he must increase exposure in accordance with the increase in distance between lens and film beyond normal (i.e., lens setting for infinity) in order to produce a correctly exposed negative or color transparency. But by what factor must the exposure indicated by an exposure meter be multiplied? The following formula provides the answer:

$$\frac{\text{lens-to-film distance} \times \text{lens-to-film distance}}{\text{focal length of lens} \times \text{focal length of lens}}$$

For example: a photographer wishes to photograph an insect, using a lens with a focal length of three inches. The distance between lens and film after focusing measures six inches. The exposure factor for this particular set-up can then be found with the aid of the following equation:

$$\text{Exposure factor} = \frac{6 \times 6}{3 \times 3} = \frac{36}{9} = 4$$

This means that the exposure indicated by the exposure meter must be multiplied by a factor of 4 if the negative is to be correctly exposed. For example, if the meter indicates an exposure of 1/100 sec. at f/16, exposure has to be four times as long and the picture must be taken either at 1/25 sec. and f/16; or 1/100 sec. and f/8; or 1/50 sec. and f/11. Any of these three combinations of shutter speed and diaphragm opening would expose the negative four times as long as the meter-indicated exposure and, in this particular case, any would produce a correctly exposed negative.

The following table lists the exposure increases (the factors by which to multiply the meter-indicated exposure) for different scales of reproduction:

ing, and auxiliary bellows. After focusing, measure the distance between lens center and film. Let's assume it is six inches. This would be equivalent to three times the focal length of the lens. To find the corresponding exposure factor, look up the "3" in the table above under "Lens-to-film distances in multiples of focal length," go down the row vertically and find, in the bottom row where the exposure factors are listed, the number "9." This is the factor by which you must multiply the exposure indicated by the exposure meter in order to produce a correctly exposed negative or color transparency. In this case, the reproduction scale (or image magnification) would be 2, i.e., the image on the film would be twice as large as the subject is in reality; this is indicated by the "2" in the second horizontal row of figures which lists the degree of image reduction or magnification, respectively.

When taking close-ups of inanimate subject matter, the photographer usually has sufficient time to calculate necessary exposure increases with the aid of the previously given formula, or to look up the respective factor in a table such as that above. But when live subjects must be photographed, time is usually much too short to consult formulas or tables, and exposure factors must be instantly available. I solved this by mounting a triple scale parallel to the auxiliary bellows of my Hasselblad single-lens reflex camera. This scale is calibrated in such a way that for each one of three interchangeable lenses (with different focal lengths) both the degree of image magnification (reproduction scale) and the corresponding exposure factor can be directly read off opposite a little pointer which is attached to, and travels with, the box of the camera. (Since this camera set-up is used exclusively for close-up shots in near-natural, natural, or more-than-natural size, it is constructed for rear-focusing, i.e., the

	Subject-to-lens distances in multiples of focal lengths					Lens-to-film distances in multiples of focal length										
	∞	100	10	5	3	2	2	2.5	3	4	5	6	7	8	9	10	11
Reproduction scale or image magnification	0	0.01	0.11	0.25	0.50	Natural size		1.5	2	3	4	5	6	7	8	9	10
Exposure factor	1	1.02	1.23	1.56	2.25	4		6	9	16	25	36	49	64	81	100	121

For example: You want to take a close-up of the head of an insect with a Leica equipped with the standard lens of two inches focal length, reflex housing, and auxiliary bellows.

front carrying the lens is solidly attached to the camera bed and focusing is accomplished by racking the camera box back and forth on tracks.) A device like this, which is of immense practical value, can be constructed for all kinds of cameras.

The scale or reproduction (i.e., the ratio of image size to subject size) is determined by the available bellows extension (maximum distance between lens and film) in conjunction with the focal length of the lens. The longer the bellows extension and the shorter the focal length of the lens, the larger the possible scale of reproduction. For example, to produce an image in natural size (scale of reproduction 1:1), the bellows extension must be twice as long as the focal length of the lens. Or, in other words, the focal length of the lens must not exceed one half of the available bellows extension. This, in conjunction with the fact that the covering power of any lens increases with decreasing distance between subject and lens, makes it possible to produce images in up to approximately ten times natural size with almost any camera featuring interchangeability of lenses. If the focal length of the lens with which the camera was originally equipped is too long to permit the photographer to make close-ups of small objects in sufficiently large scale, all he has to do is to replace the lens with a lens of shorter focal length. For example, if maximum available bellows extension (or length of extension tubes) is eleven inches, and the subject (for example, the head of a spider, *see pp. 142-143*) is to be rendered in ten times natural size on the film (scale of reproduction 10:1), a lens with a focal length not longer than one inch must be used (*see table on p. 166*). Under normal conditions, i.e., focused upon a distant object or infinity, a lens with a focal length of one inch would, of course, cover only a negative the size of a 16 mm movie frame. But, since the covering power of any lens increases as the lens-to-subject distance decreases, this one-inch lens would, in the example discussed here, cover any negative up to approximately 4x5".

Rendition of a subject in ten times natural size represents approximately the highest degree of magnification on film that is practicable under ordinary (i.e., not laboratory) conditions. Practical examples are the photographs of spider heads on pp. 142-143 which were made with a Hasselblad camera equipped with auxiliary bellows and a one-inch lens. However, at ten times magnification, the factor by which the exposure must be increased is 121 (*see table on p. 166*), depth of field is extremely

shallow, and focusing is very difficult. If higher degrees of magnification are desirable, it is usually easier to make the picture with the aid of a microscope.

I believe that "technical data" reprinted in conjunction with published photographs are generally valueless and often even misleading because other photographers might use them as a guide in their own work, not realizing that such data are almost always incomplete, often incorrect, and usually inapplicable because conditions in no two instances will be identical. For this reason, I do not include such data. Instead, I end this section with a few suggestions which, I feel, sum up the essence of my experience as a naturalist-photographer:

Be prepared. Take a camera with you even if you do not intend to make pictures. The best opportunities often happen unexpectedly. The once-in-a-lifetime chance occurs only once.

Discriminate. Some subjects should be rendered only in color. Others are most effective in black-and-white. Still others, lacking "photogenic" qualities, will always be disappointing in picture form.

Photogenic subject qualities are: simplicity, clarity, order, and organization; well-defined outline and form; contrast that is strong but not excessive; texture that can be brought out through use of surface-skimming light; pattern, rhythm, and repetition of similar forms.

Unphotogenic subject qualities are: absence of order and organization; lack of well-defined outline and form; lack of contrast; pattern and contrast which are based primarily upon color (this applies only to black-and-white photography and not to color photography); confusion of detail.

If a subject is worth photographing, it is worth photographing well. This means, if possible, one should take time to study its different aspects to determine what is typical, then emphasize what was found to be typical by making the picture when conditions are at their best. Do not limit yourself to a single view of the subject. Instead, photograph it from various distances and angles, presenting it in relation to its surroundings and in close-ups to show detail. Time and opportunity are much more valuable than film—an expendable commodity which an experienced photographer never tries to save on, knowing only too well that all his efforts may be in vain if he takes one picture too few.

Watch the illumination. Light is the medium which enables a photographer to clarify and bring out form, create contrast, suggest depth and three-dimensionality, and graphically separate objects in different planes from one another. Good illumination creates a feeling of roundness and space in the two-dimensional plane of the picture. On the other hand, illumination improperly used flattens depth and drowns form in floods of uncontrolled light. Use front light to bring out contrasty detail; side light to render texture; backlight to symbolize depth and space.

Whatever you photograph—show it clearly, in a sufficiently large scale, with crisply rendered detail. *Good* photographs show the observer *more* than he would have noticed in reality.